Life Unlimited

Dr David Lewis, D.Phil, Bsc (Hon), FIDS, is a psychologist, lecturer, broadcaster and the author of many books on psychology. He is a director of Stresswatch, a non-profit-making company which assists people with stress and anxiety problems; he is a founding trustee of Action on Phobias, a charity involved in establishing self-help groups for men and women with phobic difficulties; and he is technical director of Children Unlimited, an organisation which helps parents take a more active role in their children's education. He has spent the past ten years working on the creation of procedures for the expansion of intellectual and emotional performance and he is especially interested in the application of these methods in education, commerce and industry. He lives in Sussex.

Life Unlimited

PEAK PERFORMANCE
PAST FORTY

David Lewis

A Methuen Paperback

A Methuen Paperback

First published in Great Britain 1987
This paperback edition published 1988
by Methuen London Ltd
11 New Fetter Lane, London EC4P 4EE
Copyright © 1987 by David Lewis

Printed in Great Britain
by Cox & Wyman Ltd, Reading

British Library Cataloguing in Publication Data

Lewis, David
    Life unlimited: peak performance past
    forty.
    1. Middle age – Health and hygiene
    Rn: David Lewis Hodgson   I. Title
    613'.0434·   RA777.5

    ISBN 0–413–15580–3

My grateful thanks to David for inspiring this book and to Dr John
Storey for our many stimulating discussions on aging and his valuable
comments on the FAR programme.

'Youth is a possession you can keep
if you choose.'

Dr Herman Le Compte

Contents

Introduction

An aging revolution is underway and growing old will never be quite the same again. Two separate but interrelated factors are shaping this radical rethink of what it means to grow older.

The first is the recognition, by increasing numbers of individuals, that they must take responsibility for their own well-being. It is now widely accepted that personal health care is too important to be left entirely to the professionals, that medical science doesn't have all the answers and that it is largely in our own hands whether the gift of life is safeguarded or squandered.

We can see this quest for good health in the increasing interest in running and jogging and walking; in crowded aerobic and keep-fit classes and the rising membership of gyms and health centres; in the numbers of books on diet, nutrition and fitness published and purchased every year.

The second underlying force is the concern that declining birth rates and increasing longevity in every developed nation will make it impossible for a shrinking workforce to support large numbers of people who are inactive and chronically sick. The figures justify such fears. In 1900 only 4 per cent of Americans were in their sixties. Today the proportion of those over sixty-five has risen to 11 per cent.

Demographic studies indicate that, by the year 2000, 32 million people in the USA (12.2 per cent of the population) will live into their seventies and beyond. In 2030, when the peak created by the post-Word War II baby boom is reached, more than 18 per cent will be over sixty-five. In Britain 14.6 per cent of the population are now over sixty-five, in West Germany 15.3 per cent, in France 13.8 per cent. The Japanese too are living longer than they did before the last war, fifteen years for men and seventeen years for women; more than 9 per cent of the population is currently over sixty-five.

At the same time, all these countries have seen a substantial decrease in the birth rate as more and more couples either postpone having children or decide not to raise a family at all. West Germany currently has the lowest birth rate in Europe, at 1.3 children per woman. In England fertility has fallen by one third over the past thirteen years, and even Catholic Italy now has a lower birth rate than it had a decade ago. The French government, worried by a birth rate down from 2.7 children per woman in 1960 to 1.8 today, are offering to pay three years' 'maternal salary' to any woman having her third or fourth child.

Birth rates are now below the number needed to keep pace with death. But populations are not just declining – in Europe, America and Japan they are getting older.

One of the major consequences of this marked demographic shift is that, before the end of this century, those in work will be maintaining 25 per cent of the population in the enforced idleness of retirement. Many economists and sociologists are convinced that the only alternative to economic and social collapse lies in a drastic reversal of present assumptions about aging. Rather than writing people off once they have passed a certain age, we should make continued use of their extensive knowledge, experience, judgement and skill.

It is clear, therefore, that for society in these countries to remain viable, the majority of people must remain in peak mental and physical condition throughout their lives.

This book offers a self-help programme, based on developing the body's own natural powers of renewal, which is designed to do just that. As its sub-title suggests, I believe that this programme is especially important after the age of forty since this period of life is, for reasons which I shall explain in Chapter Two, so often the turning point in one's life. Before their fortieth birthday many men and women are able to maintain reasonable health with a minimum of effort. After the age of forty, as the body's natural powers of regeneration and recuperation become less effective, a rapid decline in mental and physical performance frequently occurs.

While this is certainly not inevitable, my research and clinical experience suggests that it is, increasingly, the norm. At least part of the reason is that the age of forty carries with it potent psychological and social implications. As I discuss in Chapter Six, the decline of hope and the growing expectation that performance, of both mind and body, must deteriorate beyond this point combine to create a powerful, self-fulfilling, prophecy of degeneration.

If you are older than forty, then do not despair. Even if you have allowed yourself to get into a poor mental and physical condition during the past years it is never too late to bring about beneficial changes and strengthen your body's inbuilt powers of regeneration. If you are younger than forty, now is an ideal time to start working with these procedures. They will enable you to lay down firm foundations on which to build a healthy, happy and fulfilling longevity.

As a psychologist whose major area of research interest lies in developing ways of enhancing human potential, I have long been interested in maintaining performance at all ages. I have also been intrigued by noticing the very great differences at which aging occurs, with some people remaining youthful right up to the end, while others suffer a slow and painful decline into senility and decrepitude.

Until 1976 my focus was on the psychology of aging, and its effects on the intellect and emotions. In that year I met the eminent Belgian gerontologist Dr Herman Le Compte at his clinic in the coastal resort of Knokke-Zoute. There I found a way of combating much of the physical deterioration associated with 'normal' aging.

Dr Le Compte treats, with great success, men and women from all walks of society and most countries of the world using therapies based on mega-multi-vitamins.

Nobody meeting him for the first time could fail to be impressed by either the strength of his personality, or his keen intelligence. Talking rapidly and eloquently in any one of ten languages, and sometimes a mixture of several at the same time, he describes with enthusiasm the mega-vitamin therapies which have made him a figure of great respect, and considerable controversy, in medical circles. His champions include not only hundreds of former patients, who know from experience the benefits to be derived from his treatments, but also such internationally repected scientists as Linus Pauling, the American chemist and twice winner of the Nobel prize; Dr Morris Rockstein of the University of Miami School of Medicine; Johan Bjorksten, who pioneered research into the causes of physical aging; and, until his death in 1985, the eminent Soviet gerontologist Dr L. V. Komarov.

Herman Le Compte has six sons and three daughters, his wife Begga d'Haese is a widely respected sculptress, and the whole family take mega-vitamin supplements, the children receiving their first doses before birth. As examples of the effectiveness of the therapy, they could hardly be more perfect. His wife, who was in her forties when I first met her, retains the appearance and complexion of a woman in her twenties, and this despite raising their large family and suffering three gruelling years in Africa. Their children are full of energy, attractive and highly gifted in both the arts and sciences. Herman Le Compte himself works a fourteen- hour day during which he supervises the work of his medical team at the clinic, writes books and edits *Rejuvenation*, the official journal of the International Association on the Artificial Prolongation of the Human Specific Lifespan, an organisation which promotes research into all aspects of aging.

The story behind Herman Le Compte's discoveries is as intriguing as the results he has obtained. It is also a tale not without a grim irony. For it was only after narrowly escaping death from a major heart attack, at the age of twenty-eight, that he started his studies of aging.

In 1954, newly qualified and just married, Dr Le Compte and his young wife arrived in the Congo to provide medical services for a local mission. Within a few weeks he had been posted to a brand-new hospital serving a population of 50,000 in an area the size of his native country. It had 300 beds, 600 patients and an average of 300 out-patients a day. Dr Le Compte was the only physician! His assistants were three European nurses, and a dozen Congolese who, although dedicated and hardworking, could neither read nor write. His operating theatre had neither electric light nor running water. As he lacked general anaesthetics even major surgery had to be performed under local anaesthesia. At night, as he worked by the light of a hissing petrol lamp, the room would swarm with insects. They crawled over his hands and eyes as he operated, and fell in such quantities into large wounds that, before stitching the incision, he had to scoop out their corpses with a kitchen ladle.

His hospital had none of the equipment normally considered essential to effective health care, no pathology laboratory or X-ray machine, no cardiac monitors or resuscitation equipment. He had only an ancient microscope which might have been useful for diagnosing malaria or parasitic worms. Since he quicky discovered that all his patients were infected with both, the microscope was left to gather dust. In three years he performed more than 3,000 operations, supervised some 2,500 births and dealt with diseases ranging from malaria to blackwater fever. Yet in all that time, he remembers, he lost only two patients.

This record is all the more remarkable because his hospital had a completely open-door policy. Frequently he accepted people turned away from other medical centres as being 'too sick' to receive treatment.

With drugs limited to local anaesthetics, penicillin and iron he was forced to treat his patients with the only substances available in any quantity – vitamins. He had thousands of bottles, jars, tubs and sacks containing vast amounts of every known vitamin. And for one good reason. Because none of the doctors at home in Belgium had any interest in or use for them, they gladly donated all the free supplies received from drug houses to the mission medics.

'Vitamins were considered valueless enough to be given away,' says Herman Le Compte, 'so we had all we needed.'

With nothing else available he administered them in large amounts. 'I would keep a patient in hospital for a few weeks before a major operation to give them a chance to rest and gather their strength,' he recalls. 'During this time they received mega-multi-vitamin injections.'

Premature births were common among the severely malnourished women who received little or no ante-natal care or instruction. Without incubators most of these babies died within hours of being born. 'Weight for a normal white infant is around 3,000 grams,' he says. 'For the child of a poor black woman it was closer to 2,000 grams. We were delivering premature babies so tiny they could be held on the palm of one hand, and weighing no more than 600 grams. Every medical report I read assured me that between 1,000 and 2,000 grams there was one-third chance of survival. Below 1,000 grams there was no hope at all.'

After reading an article in an old medical journal, Dr Le Compte decided to administer a drug called DOCA (desoxy-corticosterone acetate) which is normally used in the treatment of Addison's disease, together with mega-multi-vitamins. Using a pipette to force nourishment into mouths too tiny to take food in any other way, his nurses fed the premature babies on their mother's milk, DOCA and vitamins once each hour around the clock. More than 80 per cent of the babies survived.

From these clinical experiences, Herman Le Compte began to formulate ideas about the nature of aging – ideas which he later formalised into several widely accepted laws.

The work was unending and exhausting. He would operate on two tables at once, his nurses preparing one patient as he treated another, then finishing dressing the first as he turned his attention to the next. He drove thousands of miles to visit remote villages, often through torrential rain on the roads that were no more than mud tracks. In February 1957 he sat down behind his desk, started the first consultation of the day and collapsed with a major heart attack.

It was three months before he was well enough to return

to Belgium. It took him a further three years to regain his strength and during this time he devoted himself to reading every major book and research paper on the subject of aging. Later he travelled throughout Europe meeting gerontologists and researchers, adding to his knowledge through discussions and interviews.

In 1961 he opened his first clinic and started his lifetime's work of helping men, women and children to enjoy a healthy longevity.

Impressed by what I had seen and heard at Knokke-Zoute, I began to introduce my own clients, many of whom were suffering from intense anxiety and depression, to mega-vitamins in addition to providing psychological therapy. Later I added information about diet and exercise routines to the treatment programme. Not only was this multi-therapeutic approach far more effective in overcoming the specific problems which had brought them to see me, but most reported considerable benefits in their levels of energy, fitness and general health.

The vitamin programmes in Chapter Eight of this book owe their inspiration to the work of Dr Le Compte, although the amounts suggested in the various plans are based on my own personal and professional experience over the past ten years and are entirely my own responsibility.

The World Health Organization defines health as 'a state of complete physical, mental and social well-being and not merely the absence of disease and infirmity.' Their constitution states: 'The enjoyment of the highest attainable standard of health is one of the fundamental rights of every human being, without regard to race, religion, political belief and economic or social condition.'

Today only a small minority of the world's population are in a position to enjoy such good health. Yet, ironically, a significant proportion of those who have the great fortune to be in this position ignore their opportunities for doing so. 'It is a right which is open to you,' says Linus Pauling. 'All that you need to do is assert it by sensible behaviour.'

Much of what you will discover in this book may seem

little more than common sense. Yet when it comes to
health care common sense is often in very short supply.
There are no exotic fruits to eat, no monkey glands to
swallow, no elixirs of life to discover. But what the programmes lack in drama they do, I believe, make up for in
efficacy. They are easy to implement and follow. They
make minimum demands on your time. And, most important of all, they work.

One: Why Grow Old?

'Last scene of all, that ends this strange eventful history, is second childishness and mere oblivion, Sans teeth, sans eyes, sans taste, sans everything.'

(William Shakespeare – *As You Like It*)

The card I received on my own fortieth birthday perfectly captures the way most people feel about this milestone in their existence. 'Life begins at forty,' the message read, ' – too bad everything else spreads out, wears out and falls out!'

However willing the spirit, few doubt that by the age of forty time has taken an irreversible toll on the body. From this point on, it is widely assumed and generally accepted that mental and physical performance must inevitably nose-dive. There will be a progressive, and increasingly rapid, loss of strength, stamina, sexual potency and intellectual capacity. Enthusiasm is replaced by acceptance, energy by apathy.

The decades after forty are usually considered a time to consolidate gains made in earlier years, to reflect on past accomplishments rather than take the sort of personal and professional risks so cheerfully accepted a few years earlier.

The fact is that nothing need be further from the truth. Life after forty can become a time of even greater fulfilment, progress, growth and success. Aging need not be the unavoidable consequence of growing old. There is no reason for the performance graph to dip.

I have termed the process by which these highly desirable goals may be attained Facilitated Active Regeneration – FAR for short. This book is a practical guide to FAR's procedures and their application.

Its theme is not growing old, but *not* growing old.

Its purpose is to explain just what you can, and should, do in order to enjoy peak performance and maximum fitness after the age of forty.

Ideally, planning for peak performance past forty should begin in the thirties, or even the twenties – which is why I have included enhancement programmes for both these decades. But even if you are already forty or over, there is a tremendous amount which can be done to recapture, or retain, the stamina, vigour and youthful accomplishments of earlier years.

During research over more than a decade, I have found that Facilitated Active Regeneration can:

- Stimulate the intellect – aid creativity, problem-solving and decision-making.
- Enrich memory – leading to greater ease and accuracy of recollection and recall.
- Strengthen the body and increase stamina.
- Increase resistance to common infections by fortifying the immune system.
- Improve emotional health – and so enhance relationships.
- Enhance sexual drive.

Is aging really necessary?

The claim that aging is avoidable rather than inevitable may strike you as improbable. We are so conditioned to the notion of a relentless progression from strength to senility that the idea of opting out of growing old seems contradicted by both common sense and common experience.

Yet recent studies have shown that much of the mental and physical decline we normally associate with the passing years need never occur. 'As a result of scientific life-extension research, we no longer have to accept passively the unpleasant consequences of aging,' state Durk Pearson and Sandy Shaw in their book *Life Extension*. 'Scientific data exist demonstrating that some aspects of aging can be slowed down and even reversed.'

Not only is it now possible significantly to extend the

human life span, but we can also remain youthful in mind and body until the last moment of life. Even with our present, far from perfect, knowledge about the mechanisms of aging we can come very close to fulfilling that timeless human dream of dying young at the oldest possible age.

What FAR involves

Much of the advice given for staying healthy reminds me of the comment made by a doctor who was asked what one must do to enjoy a long life.

'Give up all enjoyable food, alcohol and every vice, especially sex,' replied the physician.

'Will that guarantee I live for ever?' asked the patient.

'No,' admitted the doctor. 'But it's going to make you feel like you have!'

FAR makes no such demands. Indeed, following the programme involves, for most people, a minimum of lifestyle change or personal inconvenience. You are not going to be asked to endure a diet of muesli in a mountain retreat, give up pleasurable activities or spend your days swathed in a tracksuit and jogging around the park. Yet despite the ease with which FAR procedures can be applied, they enhance all aspects of your performance while helping achieve the goal of a long, healthy and rewarding life.

Let me explain what Facilitated Active Regeneration in-volves, starting with the last term – regeneration.

Regeneration in action

Regeneration is the natural process by which your body continually renews itself. Even after clinical death (the termination of vital functions) some cells are still reg-enerating. Hair and nails continue growing, the liver goes on making glucose. Cells removed from the body may be suc-cessfully cultured as long as seventy-two hours after the brain has died. Absolute death only occurs after all the cells have been so chemically damaged or become so physically isolated that regeneration is no longer possible.

'Cell death,' says pathologist J. N. Webb of the Edinburgh Northern Hospital Group, 'takes place in a highly predictable manner and all the evidence points to it being genetically controlled.'

As you work and play, eat your food and read this book your body is performing this balancing act between survival and extinction, between degeneration and regeneration. At every moment part of you is dying so that the whole of you may live. 'Life depends on death,' notes biologist Dr Lyall Watson. 'We owe our lives to the cells . . . that regularly lay down their lives in internal battles dedicated to the greater glory of the organism.'

Without such sacrifices, successful development cannot occur. In the months before birth there is an unending loss and replacement of tissue. Indeed, more cells die before we are born than perish when we die! Human birth defects arise when cells programmed by nature to die at the right moment somehow survive. A failure of cells between the embryo's digits to perish on cue, for instance, produces babies with webbed hands.

When degeneration increases and regeneration is inhibited the rate of aging accelerates. There is a form of premature senility, known as progeria, which results from accelerated degeneration of the tissues, especially of the blood supply to heart and brain. One type of progeria, known as the Hutchinson-Gilford syndrome, afflicts children aged between three and four. The victims rapidly come to look like wrinkled old people, and die of old age in their early teens. A second variety, Werner's syndrome, occurs in early adult life and produces all the changes found in senescence: prematurely greying hair, loss of sight and hearing, arthritis, diabetes and hardening of the arteries. In both these cases one is seeing a dramatic loss of the system's regenerative abilities, and a subsequent acceleration of the degenerative process.

Even in mature humans, many vital systems are constantly dying and being regenerated. Around 80 per cent of the dust particles we see shimmering so poetically in a shaft of sunlight, for instance, consist of human skin. Each day we lose some 10 billion cells. In a lifetime you'll shed around forty lbs, or enough to fill a large suitcase.

These cells consist of translucent crystals, fastened

together by thin films of oil and packed with an insoluble, fibrous protein called keratin (from the Greek word meaning horny tissue). The keratin kills them in order to create a tough, flexible armour which protects the delicate, living, tissues beneath. As the outer layer self-destructs more cells are generated to take their place and die in their turn.

A similar balance between life and death can be found in the lining of the stomach, where some 35 million tiny pits produce a steady flow of gastric juices whenever the brain signals that food is – or might be – on its way. This juice is 0.5 per cent concentrated hydrochloric acid, a chemical so corrosive that it could burn through a sheet of lead. So why doesn't the stomach digest itself?

The secret of containing such a potentially self-destructive liquid can be found in some 800 million tightly wedged, baseball-bat-shaped cells forming a protective lining. These cells are destroyed so rapidly that the stomach must regenerate them at the rate of half a million per minute just to maintain the defensive wall. The result is a pink new lining for the entire stomach every three days. Normally this is capable of confining the acid within the stomach. When we are under great stress, however, the ring of muscles sealing the small intestine relax, allowing bile to surge back into the stomach.

A powerful digestive enzyme used to break up fat globules, bile is capable of digesting the stomach lining. Acid then escapes and an ulcer forms. Even then the stomach's powers of recovery are sufficient to repair the damage and replace the millions of lost cells within a few days. It is only after chronic stress has prevented the hole from healing that severe haemorrhaging can occur and emergency surgery become necessary.

This failure to repair the damage, and the fact that stress can exert such a powerful effect on the degenerative process, illustrates two crucial features of regeneration.

The first is the need to take both physical and psychological factors into account when examining causes of accelerated degeneration in normally healthy people. To enhance regeneration, therefore, we must consider all aspects of our being – physical, emotional, intellectual, sexual and social – instead of narrowly focusing on a single aspect of behaviour such as diet or exercise.

The second point is that our regenerative powers are not unlimited. When the trauma is too severe or long-lasting, permanent degeneration will occur.

Not all cells regenerate

Some cells are able to regenerate throughout life. These are called 'mitotic' from the Greek word *mitos* meaning a 'thread', because as it divides the nucleus resembles tiny threads. The cells of the skin and epithelial layer lining the digestive tract are all mitotic.

Other cells are unable to regenerate after maturity and are termed 'resting' or 'postmitotic'. These include cells in the muscles and nervous system. A heart attack, medically a myocardial infarction, may cause irreparable damage to the muscles for this very reason.

Research is being undertaken to try and discover methods for 'instructing' resting cells to switch on again and start regenerating. At present the work is confined to heart-muscle cells being cultured in laboratory containers. But if the experiments prove successful it may be possible to repeat the procedure within the human body. Should this happen a potent new weapon will have been added to the armoury of longevity.

For the present however, the only method of ensuring the continued healthy functioning of our muscles is through avoiding anything likely to hasten their degeneration while actively enhancing their stamina and vitality.

A stroke which kills brain cells produces an equally irreversible loss. Once again the inability to regenerate means that all damage is permanent. Incidentally, the once widely accepted view that up to 100,000 brain cells perish each day after the age of about thirty-five, as a natural result of aging, has been seriously challenged by gerontologists in recent years. There is, however, no doubt that postmitotic brain cells, once lost, are gone for ever.

Fortunately, all aspects of intellectual functioning, including such essential skills as memory, logical reasoning, creative thinking, problem-solving and decision-making, can be maintained at a very high level through the FAR procedures which I will be describing later in this book.

Finally, we have cells which, while they cannot divide under normal circumstances, will do so if some emergency arises. Liver cells, for instance, are usually postmitotic. If a portion of the liver is removed, or damaged, however, these cells are able to 'switch' themselves on again and regenerate the lost parts. This is an ability they share with the salamander, which is capable of growing a lost limb. It is hoped that one day amputated human arms and legs may be regenerated by discovering how to 'turn back on' postmitotic cells.

R:D – the balance of life and death

In aging we see the gradual failure of the R, or regeneration, mechanisms and the increasing ascendancy of D, cellular degeneration. Slowly at first, but with increasing speed, the system starts running down. These twin processes can be regarded as opposing ends of a continuum.

Regeneration   *Degeneration*

_____

                                    A   B   C

Up to early adulthood we occupy position A, midway between the extremes. Loss and gain are balanced, our stamina and resistance at their peak. In time, the balance shifts towards B, as the capacity for regeneration decreases while postmitotic cells become less efficient. At senility, we reach point C. The degeneration now outpaces the body's reduced ability to regenerate itself.

While physiological decline proceeds at the rate of around 1 per cent per year, some systems age faster than others. Aging is not a single, unified process, therefore, but the result of a complex interaction between many different systems. As each becomes less efficient, resistance declines and the risk of dying from even minor surgery or a trivial ailment increases significantly.

Death may finally be due to a single, malfunctioning unit such as a damaged heart, or the catastrophic destruction of a major system, as when large areas of the brain are ravaged by a cerebral stroke. Ultimately, of course, degeneration must triumph. Every living system proceeds from birth to death and decay. But the amount of time taken for the end to be reached and the degree of deterioration experienced along the way varies greatly, according to the R:D balance.

By assisting the process of regeneration while inhibiting, so far as current medical knowledge permits, degeneration we can both prolong life and safeguard health.

Avoiding harmful activities such as smoking or prolonged exposure to bright sunlight, which are known to cause cell damage, assists regeneration. The lungs of a non-smoker, for example, suffer far less degeneration than those of a heavy smoker. Skin which has never been exposed to the sun's harmful ultra-violet rays remains smoother, softer and more youthful than if tanned by constant sunshine. The buttocks of a eighty-year-old are often as smooth as the cheeks of a newborn baby.

However, while it is obviously important to avoid anything liable to accelerate degeneration, this by itself is insufficient to ensure a long and healthy life.

Active
This word emphasises the fact that its procedures are designed to reinforce our body's natural powers of regeneration, rather than merely aiming to prevent avoidable degeneration.

Facilitated
Finally, we describe the process as 'facilitated' in order to stress the need for a partnership between mind and body. It signifies the incorporation into our lifestyle of actions which assist nature in the task of prolonging vigour and vitality.

FAR – squaring the curve
There are three main approaches to aging. Some experts – called meliorists – are primarily interested in making old

age as pleasant as possible without doing anything to halt the gradual slowing-down of mind and body from middle age onwards. (See figure A on p. 10.)

Immortalists share the goal of extending life to its true genetic potential. This theoretical maximum varies between species, but in general the more active they are the less time they last. Although giant tortoises are on record as having survived for 200 years, and vultures can reach 120, the only mammal to achieve man's average three-score-years-and-ten is the Indian elephant. But does this represent our true maximum? The immortalists would argue that it does not.

Johan Bjorksten, a leading Norwegian researcher, believes the upper limit to human life is 157 years, a figure he bases on the highest age considered theoretically possible to achieve. This, Bjorksten claims, should be the primary target to achieve since anybody who fails to live as long is dying prematurely.

If he is right, then the closest anybody has come to achieving a normal lifespan in recent years was a Japanese, Shigechiyo Isumi, who died in 1986 at the age of 120. But what evidence is there that such extreme age is not merely possible but, as Bjorksten claims, what nature intended?

The best known historical example might seem to be the Sethite Methuselah, grandfather of Noah, who according to the book of Genesis lived 'nine hundred sixty and nine years'. However, recent research suggests that this seemingly phenomenal age was measured in months, giving him a lifespan of just over eighty years. There have, however, been well authenticated reports of isolated communities in which many people of both sexes survived to a great age.

A 1970 census of the Caucasus region of Georgia listed 1,884 centenarians, with a further 2,500 in neighbouring Azerbaijan, giving these regions twenty times more centenarians than the United States. Three years later, Alexander Leaf, chief of medical services at Massachusetts General Hospital, published an account of his visits to three regions of the world renowned for the longevity of their inhabitants: the Abkhazia region in the Caucasus mountains

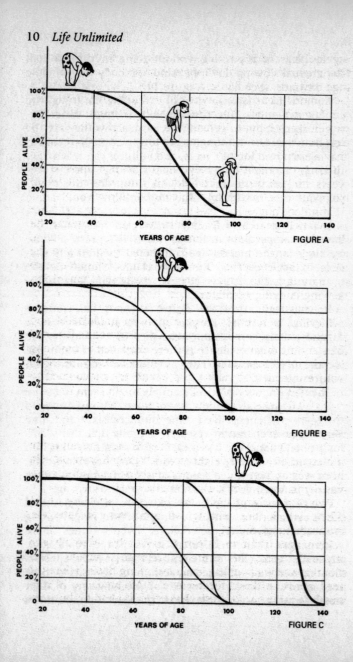

FIGURE A

FIGURE B

FIGURE C

overlooking the Black Sea, the country of the Hunza in Kashmir and Ecuador's Vilcabamba valley. Dr Leaf was able to examine many centenarians, the oldest being 'a sprightly lady named Khfaf Lasuri' who claimed to be over 130 years old. It would appear, therefore, that the immortalists' hope of prolonging human lifespan to at least double the present expectation is no wild dream. Whether it is socially desirable is another matter.

Clearly, society could only tolerate such a massive increase in lifespan, and individuals only desire it, were longevity to be combined with continued vitality.

This is the aim of the final group of researchers, who are known as incrementalists. Their concern is to eliminate the degenerative diseases normally associated with aging, enabling people to remain hale and hearty right up to the moment that life ceases. It is an approach often referred to as 'squaring the curve' since its successful application would eliminate months or years of decline. The effect of curve- squaring is shown in Figure B.

The FAR procedures involve both an immortalist and incrementalist approach to aging. The programme is aimed at extending the human lifespan, although not by anything like the doubling which may be theoretically possible, while ensuring that vigour and health are maintained to the last (see Figure C).

We all age differently

You've only got to look at friends and relatives to appreciate the different rates at which people grow old – in other words, how much more rapidly degeneration gains mastery in some people than others.

Two of my clients typify this extreme variability in the effects which the passing of time has on attitude, appearance and ability.

John, aged fifty-two, is lean, fit and active. Mentally and physically alert, he exercises regularly, enjoys rifle-shooting and windsurfing, and works long hours, when the need arises, without feeling overly fatigued. He is constantly looking out for fresh challenges, both in his business life and leisure activities, enjoys life to the full and looks forward to each new day.

Martin, although eight months younger, gives the appearance of being his senior by a good ten years. He is paunchy and balding, his poor complexion reflecting a generally unhealthy lifestyle and lack of fitness. He is prone to infections and has to take to his bed several times a year with colds or flu. He avoids vigorous exercise, feels constantly fatigued and finds it impossible to sustain his enthusiasm or concentration for long.

It is clear that Martin is aging more rapidly than John, and that his lifestyle is a major factor in that accelerated deterioration of mental and physical health.

Yet, when I first met them, some fourteen years ago, their roles were reversed. At that time John was over-weight, in poor health and suffering a variety of stress-related ailments. He had frequent migraines, had endured low back pains for years and suffered from high blood pressure. Martin, on the other hand, was a slim, physically fit sportsman whose spare-time activities included sailing and horseriding. He ran a large and flourishing manu-facturing company, and put in punishingly long hours without feeling especially fatigued.

The transformation, in one case for the better and in the other case for the worse, happened around their fortieth birthday. The decisions they made at this time resulted in John embarking on a new lifestyle which enhanced his inborn powers of regeneration, while Martin started on a journey that resulted in the accelerated degeneration of his mental and physical prowess.

It is a moment of decision every one of us makes, con-sciously or unconsciously, at some time in our life – most usually around forty. Just why this age is so critical to healthy longevity will be discussed in Chapter Two. Typically, we choose to move away from a healthy lifestyle, which is permitting maximum natural regeneration of the system while minimising degenerative changes, towards a way of living which, with varying degrees of speed, shifts us away from regeneration and towards decline.

In 1832 an English actuary, Benjamin Gompertz, formulated a mathematical law which allows the chances of dying at any age to be calculated. Gompertz's Law states that the probability approximately doubles every eight years from puberty onwards. This is a helpful calculation if you are in the business of writing life assurance policies. But where your chief interest lies in prolonging youthful life, another law of aging assumes far more significance. Formulated by the eminent Belgian gerontologist Dr Herman Le Compte, it specifies the conditions under which people will age most rapidly.

The aging law of Le Compte

As I explained in the introduction, Le Compte has formulated some important basic laws about how and why we age. The first and most important of these states: 'Aging proceeds most rapidly where the deficiencies are greatest and most numerous.'

Deficiencies, which may be physical (i.e. diet, exercise, environment) or psychological (loneliness, depression, anxiety, stress, boredom and so on) weaken our powers of regeneration, so making it easier for the degenerative process to gain command.

Once started, this decline frequently becomes self-perpetuating as each deficiency makes another more likely. Poor nutrition, for instance, can lead to depression and lethargy. The resulting lack of stimulation and exercise depresses appetite still further.

Table One, below, illustrates Le Compte's first law in action across social classes. The *plus* figures indicate the

Table 1

	Cause of Death					
	Tuberculosis	Coronary Disease	Lung Cancer	Duodenal ulcer	Bronchitis	Stomach Cancer
Unskilled	+85	+12	+48	+73	+94	+63
Semi-Skilled	+ 8	− 4	+ 4	+ 7	+16	+14
Skilled	− 4	+ 6	+ 7	− 4	− 3	+ 1
Managerial	−46	− 5	−28	−25	−50	−37
Professional	−60	− 2	−37	−52	−72	−51

degree of risk above average of a person dying for the reason given. A *minus* number shows the extent to which the risk falls below average.

As the table clearly shows, social class plays a significant part in the likelihood of succumbing to any of the major causes of death in the Western world. In every case the risks are greatest for those in the unskilled and semi-skilled groupings.

There may be many reasons why this is so. Diet could be less nourishing; less healthy exercise – as opposed to often unhealthy physical labour – taken; working conditions could be more hazardous and there might be less knowledge about ways of protecting one's health.

In each case, the underlying factor is the degree, and magnitude of, the age accelerating deficiencies present in their lives.

Impoverished diets

Many people believe they eat sensibly, while following a diet which is, actually, significantly harmful to their health. This is partly due to the great increase, over the past few years, of high carbohydrate 'junk' foods, often low in protein and lacking vitamins and vital trace elements. Other dietary deficiencies result from the way food is processed in factories, from delays in transporting it from farm to table, and from inefficient cooking.

Refining grains to produce white flour makes excellent commercial sense because refined grains store better and white bread is still more popular than the very dark brown loafs made from natural grains. But, apart from removing important roughage, refining removes essential B vitamins which are only partially replaced by the refiners. Foods preserved by canning, steaming or freezing lose many vitamins, including E which, as we shall see, has a life-prolonging, cell-protecting, function.

Other vitamins are lost because the food gets stale before it can be sold. Eggs, for instance, are an excellent source of vitamins A and D, B1 (thiamin) and B2 (riboflavin). But they start to deteriorate immediately after laying. Even eggs sold as 'fresh from the farm' have been found in surveys to be up to five days old. After even this relatively short time much of their nutritional value has disappeared.

Overcooking green vegetables results in the loss of water-soluble vitamin C, another substance which has a life-prolonging, protective effect on the cells.

Add to these deficiencies impoverished eating habits and it quickly becomes apparent why even those who never go hungry could be denying themselves the raw materials their systems need for a long and healthy life.

Yet even when a satisfactory diet of fresh, wholesome food is eaten there will still be a deficiency in certain vitamins. While these are not going to produce such health problems as rickets or scurvy, they will be sufficient to encourage the cellular degeneration associated with 'normal' aging.

Inadequate exercise

During medical examinations, military doctors are frequently horrified at the condition of the young recruits who come before them. At an age when they should be at their physical peak, up to half of them often have circulation problems usually associated with the elderly. Their arteries are clogged and hardened, producing the arteriosclerosis which is a major factor in strokes and coronary heart disease. Although in their late teens and early twenties, they may have bodies far more typical of unfit males in their forties.

Like any complex piece of machinery designed and built for activity, the body needs to be constantly exercised in order to remain in good shape. It is one important way of prolonging the active life of non-regenerating, postmitotic muscle cells. I shall be explaining the best ways of exercising in Chapter Ten.

Hazardous environments

Noise, dust, dirt, toxic chemicals, poor ventilation, over-crowding and the stress of overwork are commonplace urban hazards. While much will be unavoidable, it is often possible to take sensible precautions by reducing exposure and minimising the risks. Regular visits to the countryside and the sea, or city parks, provide a chance to breath cleaner and better oxygenated air.

Improved ventilation, sound-proofing and clean work areas result in significant gains in performance and morale, as well as safeguarding health. Information, easily gleaned from the vast numbers of books and magazines now devoted to healthier living, can also safeguard you against avoidable hazards.

Loss of interest

There is, however, one deficiency which can be found across all social classes – a loss of interest in life. Once this is lost, there's very little reason for going on living. Being interested means more than simply having a hobby to fill in your free time and a job to occupy your working hours. It means engaging in activities which keep mind and body stimulated and vigorous. Sadly, most people fail to maintain their level of interest and involvement, often using the excuse of retirement to flee into a life of idleness.

The very name used to describe residences for the elderly – rest homes – emphasises the widely held belief that the end of full-time employment spells the end of any active life. I shall be discussing the influence of negative social attitudes on accelerated aging in the next chapter.

I can illustrate the importance of sustaining one's interest in life, right up to the last moment of life, by describing the effect of mental attitudes on the lives of two men. Both retired in their early sixties, but their lifestyle from then on was very different.

Immediately after leaving his teaching post, the first – a professor of medicine at a leading medical school – founded an institute for the study of aging which rapidly gained international recognition. Today, aged over ninety, he spends much of his time travelling, lecturing, writing and broadcasting. He has added considerably to the academic and social successes which he achieved earlier in his career and leads a life which is varied, stimulating and productive. Each day is a challenge to be savoured. He wants to live.

My second client once headed a multi-national brokerage firm. He had made no plans for his retirement, beyond playing more golf. He considered that his years of hard work had entitled him to a life of idleness and he looked forward eagerly to taking things more easily. After only two years he found golf far less appealing as a major activity and started spending more time around the house, doing odd jobs and watching a great deal of television.

Because he and his wife had wanted to escape from the stress of city life, they had sold their apartment and bought a large, remote house in the country. This meant leaving their friends behind and they found it hard to make new ones. After his wife died, he became isolated both physically and mentally, turning into a recluse who seldom left the house. He took little exercise, and met few people. He felt constantly unwell. He had nothing to look forward to and no reason to remain alive. At the age of sixty-eight he died.

A negative sense of self is a major 'deficiency', leading as the law of Le Compte would indicate to an acceleration of the aging process. A strong, positive self-image, by comparison, greatly contributes to the regeneration process.

The age traps in action

As the years pass it is all too easy to become trapped in a vicious circle of decline, and the point at which this downward spiral commences is getting earlier and earlier in a society still obsessed with youth culture.

Under the pressure of establishing themselves in career and family life, many men and women abandon the healthy lifestyle of their early teens and allow deficiencies to start undermining their systems. By the age of forty the amount of degeneration which has already occurred may be significant. The result, as predicted by the first law of Le Compte, is accelerated aging and deteriorating mental and physical health.

The depressing statistic is that 28 per cent of American

males and 15 per cent of American females celebrate their fortieth birthday in such poor shape that they never reach their sixtieth. During this period two major factors are at work producing deficiencies.

The first is a high level of stress. The second, ironically, is the degree of physical fitness enjoyed by the average person at the onset of this period, that is at the end of their teens. In the developed nations a reasonable diet, combined with extensive medical care and exercise, build stamina and endurance during childhood and adolescence so that the majority of young people embark on adult life with ample reserves of mental and physical strength on which they can draw.

This means that they are able to take considerable punishment over a long period of time without, seemingly, suffering accelerated degeneration. They can smoke, drink to excess, take little exercise, eat unsound meals, work long hours and tolerate a great amount of stress and still look and feel in great shape.

It's like having a car which appears shiny and new on the outside, while rotting away with rust from the inside. Until a crisis occurs and the bodywork starts to collapse, nobody realises how extensive and considerable is the extent of the decay.

Each year, millions of apparently healthy men in their forties suffer an untimely end due to coronary heart disease. Others become victims of a variety of psychogenic disorders such as ulcers, migraines, back pains and reduced resistance to infection.

Perhaps you have recognised something of your own lifestyle in those comments? If so, you may be wondering what you can, realistically, be expected to do about it. You see nothing wrong with being ambitious, working hard or wanting to live comfortably, and you are perfectly right to feel this way.

The FAR programme is not an alternative to any of these aims or activities. Nor is it incompatible with them. In order to inhibit degeneration you will have to either eliminate, or greatly reduce, some actions which are inevitably damaging to your health, such as smoking and poor eating habits. You will also have to set aside some time to build up your powers of regeneration. But neither of these requirements prevents one from being hard-working and achievement-orientated. Indeed, by enhancing your mental and physical health, the time invested in such activities should have a beneficial effect on your overall performance.

But, as important as preventing physical deficiencies is developing a new attitude of mind towards the aging process. Another of Le Compte's laws states: 'Good health is a possession we can keep – if we choose.'

If in answer to the question 'Do you really want to achieve peak performance past forty?' your reply is 'Yes, but only if I can do so without changing any of my age-accelerating habits', then FAR cannot help. If, on the other hand, you are willing to break some bad habits and undertake new, regeneration-enhancing habits then to reach forty is no longer to arrive at a watershed but to embark on a period of even greater accomplishment. To make that choice you don't have to retreat from the world and live on a desert island on goats' milk and wholemeal bread. You need not spend every spare minute in a gym, or every lunchtime in a healthfood restaurant. You do not have to give up being ambitious or hardworking.

The six keys to Facilitated Active Regeneration

1 Social attitudes towards aging, determined mainly by calendar years, create a death curse which by changing self-image and undermining self-esteem and one's sense of competence, produces deficiencies which hasten degeneration while impeding regeneration. It is essential not to allow these potent and punishing beliefs to influence your outlook or performance. I shall be exploring these in more detail in the next chapter.

2 At the start of the FAR programme you will undertake a detailed analysis of your current lifestyle, in order to determine the extent to which you may be encouraging efficient regeneration or promoting rapid degeneration. By assessing yourself every three or four months, you can check on the gains which have been achieved and identify remaining

barriers to healthy longevity and enhanced performance. You will find these assessments in Chapters Three and Four.

3 Mental attitude is crucial to Facilitated Active Regeneration. If you believe you are declining, degeneration is accelerated. Never say, or think, anything likely to undermine your self-confidence – such as: 'It's only to be expected at my age . . .' – and you will greatly strengthen your body's natural powers of regeneration.

4 As we shall see in Chapter Four, physical aging is a disease of the metabolism whose degenerative consequences may be slowed through a combination of vitamin therapy, diet and exercise.

5 The FAR programme adopts a whole-person approach. You cannot tackle degeneration in just one area – for instance by taking more exercise – and expect fully to protect yourself against degeneration in other areas.

6 To use FAR procedures successfully, you must appreciate that there is nothing 'normal' about what we usually consider to be *normal* aging. There is no longer any need to become the helpless victim of passing years. You can take control of the aging process at any age.

Why grow old, when peak performance past forty is such an attractive and attainable goal?

Two: Avoiding the aging traps

'No frumps, fatties or over forties!'
(Sign on entrance to New York disco)

While there is truth in the cliché 'You are as young as you feel,' it might be more accurately stated as 'You are as young as you are allowed to be.'

Dr Alex Comfort has coined the term *agism* to describe the negative social attitudes which prove so harmful to a healthy longevity. 'Agism is a notion that people cease to be people,' he explains. 'They cease to be the same people or become people of distinct and inferior kind by virtue of having lived a specified number of years.'

These attitudes are, typically, rooted in what should be the least important element in how old we feel, the number of birthdays notched up. Calendar age dominates the lives of most people, affecting not only how others regard us but how positively we view our own abilities and capacities. As I explained in the previous chapter, a negative sense of self is a major 'deficiency', leading as the First Law of Le Compte predicts to an acceleration of the aging process. A strong, positive self-image, by comparison, greatly contributes to the regeneration process.

At the age of thirty-nine Peter was a fit, successful company executive. Intelligent, creative and confident, he tackled each new challenge with enthusiasm. Then came his fortieth birthday.

While this has absolutely no medical importance it does have considerable personal, and social, implications for most people, since it has become a significant landmark along life's way. Comments about being over the hill, jokes emphasising his inevitable intellectual, physical and sexual deterioration, jests that he is past his best, may provoke laughter but they also give rise to doubts. 'Better start taking life more easily now I've hit middle-age,' Peter told his wife.

Although he felt as fit and ambitious as ever, he found it hard to shrug off the years of powerful social conditioning which comes from living and working in an acutely age-conscious culture. The halfway mark along the traditional road of 'three-score-year-and-ten' is now well behind him. 'I'll have to slow down a bit,' he worries. 'My system can't put up with the same level of stress it endured so easily a few years ago.'

Because he expects his body to be less capable of physical exertion, Peter stops taking as much exercise. This creates a self-fulfilling prophecy as strength, stamina and vitality nose-dive.

He tires more readily and starts paying far more attention to previously ignored minor aches and pains. These increase his conviction that his body is going into a sharp decline. Poorer physical health, aggravated by loss of confidence, lower his self-esteem. His fears for the future increase apparent intellectual deterioration. He notices, and comments bitterly on, every slip, each blunder, any lack of concentration or failure of memory. The truth is that these mistakes are neither more serious nor more frequent than in previous years. The difference is that he now pays far more attention to them, and sees them as evidence of age-related decline.

Anxiety also makes it more likely that these errors are going to occur. So, in a very short time, he sets up a self-fulfilling prophecy of inadequacy. Risks are regarded not as challenges but threats.

Not that Peter is alone in this respect. Studies of men and women engaged in potentially dangerous sports, such as sky-diving, parachuting and canoeing, have shown that after forty, activities once seen as stimulating are more likely to be considered unacceptably hazardous.

'New jobs are hard to find after forty,' Peter reflects

anxiously. 'Nobody wants to employ somebody past their best. Don't stick your neck out. Play safe.'

So a once-innovating executive settles into some secure niche to await the release of retirement. Enthusiasm is replaced by apathy. Self-confidence gradually gives way to uncertainty. Regeneration slows. Degeneration grows. Gradually at the start, but with gathering momentum, Peter's mind and body slither and slide down a spiral of decline.

It's never too late to bring about improvements, of course. Change for the better is always possible, at any age and from any physical condition. But Peter is soon so trapped by the negative belief that such deterioration is unavoidable that he takes no serious steps to improve matters. In the ten years between forty and fifty he ages nearly twenty.

And don't think it could never happen to you! Even if you are currently working hard, and effectively, at enhancing regeneration – through exercise, diet and a positive attitude towards life – the risk remains. So long as you remain susceptible to aging propaganda, you are vulnerable to accelerated degeneration.

To understand why this should happen, we need to appreciate the central role in all our lives of various kinds of hierarchies.

Hierarchies and your health

Hierarchies arise whenever humans, or social animals, gather together. They serve the valuable evolutionary purpose of establishing stable relationships and reducing aggression within the group.

In successful animal societies the authority of the dominant animal is rarely challenged and, as a result, the group can devote all its resources to hunting for food and protecting their young against predators, rather than squandering effort and energy on fighting with each other. Being at the top of the pecking order confers such privileges as feeding before the others, having the pick of the females and the choice of sleeping spot.

From the earliest years of life we are members of one sort of hierarchy or another. At home, at school and at work.

Studying the non-verbal behaviour of children in play-school, it soon became clear to me that even at the age of two or three the majority of these infants were not only conscious of the pecking order in their group but eagerly competed for their place within it. Toys which had a high status, because they were in limited supply and much sought after by all the children, would be fought over and struggled for. But once that treasure had been won, and displayed by the proud possessor, it would be swiftly discarded. What clearly mattered was not the fun the toy provided but the status its ownership conferred.

In most commercial organisations, an individual's position within the company hierarchy is clearly defined and, as in the playschool, identified by various status symbols. Your position in the hierarchy determines how many people will defer to you and must be deferred to in turn. Since space is costly in any major city, office size usually increases according to rank, as do such other trappings of success as furnishings, the depth of carpet, the opulence of the company car, and the elegance of the dining- and wash-rooms.

'Success and failure could be seen in the size, decor and location of offices,' writes the former Nixon aide John Dean in *Blind Ambition*. 'Anyone who moved to a smaller office was on his way down. If a carpenter, cabinetmaker or wallpaper-hanger was busy in someone's office, this was a sure sign he was on the rise.'

In many hospitals, senior medical staff enjoy waitress service at small tables covered with fresh linen, have a choice of food and wines and dine off expensive china. Meanwhile workers lower in the hierarchy queue for their meals at self-service counters and dine off formica-topped tables in crowded canteens. During a recent strike at one hospital, when the laundry was working under great pressure with a minimum staff, and could handle only the most urgent cleaning jobs, table cloths for the consultants' dining-room were considered as essential as sheets and dressings.

The importance attached to symbols indicating position in the hierarchy are considerable. The key to the executive wash-room means more to many ambitious executives than a rise in salary.

A less clearly defined, but no less significant, hierarchy exists in some homes. Children are normally expected to defer to the wishes of parents, who say what behaviour will or cannot be tolerated, who is allowed into the home and who is not.

For most people, therefore, one's position in a particular hierarchy, and the symbols by which rank is recognised, are of major importancce. Far from being merely the outward trappings of accomplishment and indications of one's standing in society, they become a fundamental part of one's sense of self. Ask the majority of people what they do, and they'll tell you what they work at.

Redundancy or retirement can shatter self-esteem not just as a result of the threat to financial security but because job loss destroys a major part of many people's identity. 'He is the happiest man who can trace an unbroken connection between the end of his life and the beginning,' wrote Goethe in *Maxims and Reflections*. By their abrupt, unavoidable and damaging intrusions into the flow of one's existence, these age-related changes shatter such continuity. Often the consequences, which can include deep depression, anxiety, loss of confidence, apathy, despair and physical illness, are so severe that the individual never really recovers.

A long-term study of the effects of unemployment, by physician Norman Beale, has shown that the health of people affected continues to deteriorate more than three years after the redundancy took place. Cardiologist Peter Nixon links loss of a place in a hierarchy with the onset of heart disease:

> The essence of this conflict is a frustration of the tendency to dominate at work or in the family, or both, coupled with frustration of the desire for admiration and social recognition. There may have been a failure (real or threatening) to ascend the social ladder, a set-back in salary or position at work . . . chronic or recurrent financial worries or a real or threatening acute financial catastrophe – all this occurring in spite of hard and intensive work which in the view of the subjects should have called for recompense rather than for frustration.

Our position in the hierarchy and our ability to retain, or improve upon, the status it affords is determined, to a considerable extent, by something which lies entirely outside personal human control – our age.

In medicine, age is indicated by physical changes such as greying hair and failing eyesight, known as biomarkers. In society the most important and inflexible of all biomarkers is the birth certificate. Grey hair can be hidden, poor eyesight restored by discreet contact lenses. But short of major forgery the birth-certificate biomarker cannot be disguised.

Certain ages trigger unavoidable changes in our lifestyle. They also, as we have just seen, produce major changes in people's attitudes towards us. Below certain ages you cannot be held criminally responsible, have legal sexual intercourse, get into debt, fight for your country or drink alcohol. Above other ages you find increasing difficulties in getting car insurance, finding a job, starting a training programme or embarking on a new career. In many organisations it is against established policy to promote people above a certain age into higher-status jobs. And after a particular birthday, which is getting lower all the time, retirement becomes compulsory.

Such decisions are made not on your merits as a human being but automatically and without right of appeal, often for the sake of bureaucratic or legislative convenience.

In the seventeenth century most officials died in office and were respected for their age and wisdom. Indeed many attempted to add to their years by powdering their hair and wearing the style of clothes favoured by the aged. In France much of the deference afforded the elderly disappeared during the French Revolution with its notions of equality. By the end of the eighteenth century the mood was such that mandatory retirement laws were enacted in some parts of the United States.

The selection of sixty-five for men and sixty for women as the start of pensionable age, for instance, was not based on any kind of medical considerations, but with an eye to saving the State as much money as possible. These ages were arbitrarily established by the German Chancellor Otto von Bismarck when, in 1889, he established the world's first social security pension scheme. The laudable aim was to remove the scandal of the destitute elderly, but underlying those charitable intentions was a shrewd determination not to be any more generous than was necessary with public funds. At that time life expectancy at birth was only thirty-seven!

Today, these chronological milestones have become so firmly enshrined in Western social and business practice that the able and healthy are forced into a life of idleness along with the decrepit and incompetent. As individuals accept the role of 'old person' they start to expect less of themselves – professionally, sexually, and physically – and so create a self-fulfilling prophecy of decline. By putting mind and body on to 'idle', they introduce deficiencies which encourage deterioration while inhibiting regeneration.

The power of the mind to affect physical health and aging will be considered in more detail in Chapter Six. Where negative social attitudes are concerned its influence must never be underestimated. In Australia, Aboriginal witchdoctors have long been able to induce the death of previously strong and healthy young adults by going through a ritual that puts them under a curse of death. Medical science is generally impotent to prevent the victims, once cursed, from becoming steadily weaker until, on the precise time and date ordained by the magician, life ceases.

Similar death rituals can be found in African and Caribbean voodoo magic. In our culture the death curse involves gold watches rather than animal bones, and presentation dinners instead of animal sacrifice, yet these differences do not mean that the effects are any less powerful. Within a short time of entering retirement, many victims go into a rapid decline, become less intellectually alert, less emotionally vital and less physically robust.

Alex Comfort likens the agism implicit in such policies to racism, since both are 'based on fear, folklore and the hang-ups of a few unlovable people. . . . Like racism it needs to be met by information, contradiction and, when necessary, confrontation.'

Among the more damaging myths of agism are:

Myth Failing health and chronic illness are natural elements of the normal aging process.

Fact Those aged over sixty-five have an average of 1.3 acute illnesses a year, compared with 2.1 for all other ages. As Leslie Kenton emphasises in her book *Ageless Ageing*,

> Throughout history most medical traditions – from China and India to ancient Sumeria – have taught that degeneration is *not* a normal part of the aging process, that provided we recognise the biological laws by which we are constituted and live with respect for them, we can live to a great age free of arthritis, heart attacks, cancer, lung disease and the rest.

Myth Human lifespan has already been extended as far as is either possible or desirable by advances in medicine.

Fact I am often criticised for advocating the FAR programme by people worried about population growth. They insist that it is desirable for people to die as rapidly as possible to make room for the younger generation. There are three points to be made.

First, and not surprisingly, it is typically somebody else's demise they are advocating, rarely their own or those they love. Secondly, as I have pointed out, birth rates in all the developed countries are falling, so Western society urgently requires more fit, healthy and active people, not less. Finally, if aging inevitably led to the deterioration and dependency which underlies many people's fears about growing old, then it would be irresponsible to advocate it. Nor would anyone with any sense desire such a grim fate. But, as I demonstrate in this book, it need never be a choice between early death or unavoidable senility.

You can preserve health, vitality, intellectual capacity and physical fitness right up the moment when the last breath leaves your body. Such a goal is not merely personally highly desirable, it is also socially essential. The wisdom and experience of older people, when respected and fully utilised by society, can enrich the lives of us all.

Myth As you get older you get slower in mind and body.

Fact The error of this widely accepted myth was recently demonstrated by Drs Harold Greeley and Alexander Reeves at the Dartmouth Medical School in New Hampshire. Their research showed that the average loss in reaction time is only 1.4 *thousandths* of a second per year after the age of twenty.

This amounts to a loss of no more than one-tenth of a second in sixty years. The finding has even greater significance than might at first appear. Commenting on their work in the American health care magazine *Prevention*, Alexander Reeves, chairman of the School's neurology department, explained that reaction time is a measure of more than merely the speed of response: 'We were really testing cognition, or thinking. Generally, eighty-year-olds solve problems just as well as twenty-year-olds, given just a little more time. People who eat good diets and continue to exercise and be involved in their environments may even improve their brain's power of cognition.'

Myth Your sense of adventure disappears and all you require for peace of mind is a quiet, uneventful life.

Fact The trouble is that obvious exceptions to this notion – such as Coco Chanel, the Parisian dress designer who made a triumphant comeback at the age of seventy-one; Dame Sybil Thorndike, the actress who published a book at ninety; or Marian Hart, who flew solo across the Atlantic when aged eighty-four – are viewed as rare exceptions to a general rule, instead of people achieving a potential available to almost all.

Our unexploited potential

A failure to realise one's true intellectual and physical potential is not confined to the over-sixties. In fact, Dr Joseph Still of California suggests that no more than 5 per cent achieve this goal at any age.

The figures below illustrate actual and theoretical levels of accomplishment, which Dr Still has calculated for a variety of physical and intellectual activities. The lower line represents the sort of performance most people manage at different times during their life. The upper line indicates what might have been achieved.

The first figure charts the physical rise and decline of the average man and woman experiencing the wide range of deficiencies found in the normal lifestyle. Their diet may be inadequate, they take insufficient exercise, smoke, drink too much and so on.

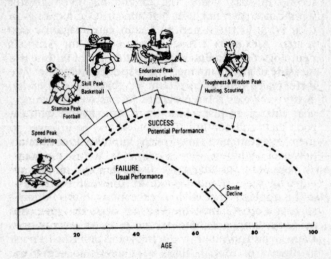

Up to the age of thirty the body's regenerative powers are sufficient to cope with this sort of punishment without obvious signs of wear and tear. But from this point on, observed performance starts to decline.

Since every sport demands different degrees and combinations of speed, strength, suppleness and stamina, and since certain periods of our life produce an optimum combination of these qualities for each type of activity, the upper line depicts them as peaking at different ages.

The second figure plots the wide discrepancy between actual and potential intellectual accomplishments. As with physical abilities, mental skills peak at different times during life.

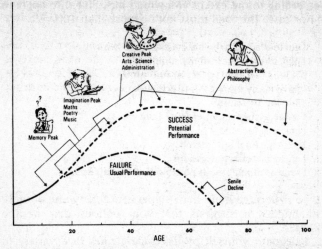

Dr Still considers that, usually, there is a drastic decline in mental capacity after the age of forty. Not because the brain cells deteriorate, but because of the damage caused by adopting an increasingly pessimistic view about one's intellectual abilities.

By following the FAR programme you can expect to enjoy far higher levels of performance in all areas of endeavour at any age.

Here are six practical steps to prevent society from hounding you to an early grave.

One – Create multiple hierarchies

Most people operate in two major hierarchies, both extremely age-sensitive: their work and the family. The first is at risk from retirement, redundancy, takeover, restructuring, dismissal and financial failure. The second can be threatened by marital upsets, conflicts with children, the break-up of the family as offspring grow up and leave home and so on.

You can check the extent to which such a dependency exists by allocating each of the statements below a percentage according to the extent you would most like it to apply in your case. The total must not be more than 100.

I am looked up to by my colleagues at work
I play an active role in my community
I belong to a sports or social club/group
I have many more goals to achieve at work
I live for my family
I enjoy leisure activities more than work
I am very sociable
I seek spiritual fulfilment
I enjoy material possessions
I send as much time as possible with my children

If you allocated more than 30 per cent to any one of those statements, it suggests that your options may be too limited.

Safeguard yourself by developing roles in a variety of hierarchies, each of which provide the level of satisfaction and status you seek. This could mean joining a local society, and either staying as a member or having ambitions to run for office. You might consider becoming a school governor, assisting a charity, joining a health tribunal, running for public office, organising a youth club, serving as a part-time instructor or youth leader.

Do whatever appeals. But never depend on just one or two hierarchies.

Two – Anticipate change

Somebody once remarked that the only person who really looks forward to change is a wet baby. But whether we relish the prospect or not our very survival depends on being able to adapt to changes.

At work change may involve greater responsibilities, a company reorganisation, a merger, departmental restructuring, working under a different boss. Often these will require personal changes as well: moving to a new area, making fresh friends, leaving behind relatives. Children leaving home, the breakdown of a relationship, losing a partner through death or divorce are all potentially health-endangering changes.

Although significant changes will always arouse anxiety and prove difficult to cope with, their effects can be minimised provided you have other options open to you, such as the warm, secure and unwavering support of an intimate partner and good physical health.

When there are equally viable alternatives to enjoy, then even a major change seems less catastrophic. Good health allows you to resist infections which might otherwise take advantage of your weakened immune system. But of these conditions, having a companion to discuss your difficulties and share your anxieties is probably the most critical.

In a major study of the emotional health of London women, George Brown and Tirril Harris of Bedford College, found that the greatest safeguard against becoming severely depressed in the face of traumatic life events was a loving spouse.

Three – Reject agism
Refuse to accept that you are a special kind of person simply because a certain number of years have passed since your birth. Challenge all of society's assumptions about aging, whether they involve physical health, emotional stability, intellectual ability or sexual needs and capacities.

Four – Never say never
Constantly explore and expand your horizons. Take a chance. Try new things. Never automatically rule out doing something or attempting anything because you might be 'too old'.

American gerontologist Dr Walter Alvarez offers this description of a biologically young person: 'One who still has the ability to conceive, initiate, adopt, activate and operate new ideas, including those of others, no matter how radically new they may be.'

Five – Assert yourself

This is a trait most associated with the very young. But it is a powerful health enhancer at any age. If you want something don't be afraid to ask for it. If you've a right for something then demand it. In the young such an attitude is usually admired and described as determination. As the years pass it is more likely to be considered pig-headedness. If impudence helps you retain control over your destiny, then being called pig-headed is a small price to pay.

Six – Be yourself

You can only do this by rejecting unreasonable demands that you conform to society's expectations, remaining involved with and interested in life and keeping physically healthy. FAR procedures help you do all three.

The last enemy

'What is it to grow old?' asked the poet Matthew Arnold, and answered his own query with a long and miserable litany of all the misfortunes that may afflict us. It is, he claimed,

> . . . to spend long days
> And not once feel that we were ever young;
> It is to add, immured
> In the hot prison of the present, month
> To month with weary pain.

In the 130 years since those lines were written more people will have shared his gloomy opinion than have dreamed of viable alternatives.

Today we can say, with increasing certainty, that it does not have to be like that. According to the Soviet philosopher I. V. Vishev:

> Everyone must be aware of the great fact that the life of man is an absolute and enduring value. Death, including the natural one, is the most terrible and irreparable misfortune, a flagrant evil, to which it is inadmissable to reconcile oneself. As long as

man lives he retains the possibility of solving all problems that
face him, of achieving noble purposes. . . . In the name of and
for the benefit of man it is necessary to succeed in attaining his
practical immortality.

Although the last enemy can never be defeated, there is no
longer any need to offer easy victory through abject
surrender.

The FAR solution is to enhance all aspects of living by
developing a lifestyle which enhances your body's natural
powers of regeneration. Only in this way can one ensure
the consistent self-renewal essential for maintaining peak
performance throughout life.

Three: Discovering your secret ages

> 'Planning is bringing the future into the present so that you can do something about it now.'
>
> (Alan Lakein, *How To Get Control of Your Time and Your Life*)

When asked our age, we usually reckon it from the date of birth, perhaps deducting a few years from misplaced vanity. Indeed, the very fact that so many people feel obliged to lie about their age is an excellent indication of the concern felt over growing old. Yet the number of birthdays celebrated is only one measure, and not an especially helpful one, of aging. As we saw in Chapter One, people grow older at very different rates and any useful measure of longevity needs to take these individual differences into account.

When creating an effective FAR programme for yourself the number of years you have lived is much less important then how you have lived them. For this reason, the starting point is to determine your personal aging profile based on the balance between regeneration and degeneration which you are currently managing to achieve. This profile must take into account both physical and psychological aging, since body and mind are intimately linked.

We each grow older in four very different ways, and often at different rates within these aging processes. These are our secret ages, since we are mostly unaware even of their existence, let alone their influence on how we act, think and feel.

Dr James Birren, head of the gerontology centre at the University of Southern California has identified three types of age and aging: biological, psychological and social. In my work I have found it helpful to include one other:

intellectual aging. This is because the efficiency with which we are able to use our intellects plays a major role in personal expectations and social attainment. On many occasions, clients in their mid-forties and early fifties have expressed fears that their memory was letting them down, that they were less creative or mentally alert than even a few years earlier. In most cases such anxiety was groundless, and the defects were rapidly corrected using FAR mind- enhancement procedures. However, while the fears persisted they had a generally depressing influence on many aspects of regeneration.

For this reason we shall be creating an aging profile based on a total of four factors:

- *Biological aging* – is the rate at which different groups of your cells are becoming progressively less capable of effective functioning.
- *Psychological aging* – relates to your ability to develop and sustain loving relationships, deal with life's inevitable ups and downs, and manage your emotions.
- *Intellectual aging* – involves the efficiency with which your brain functions, especially when learning new skills, acquiring fresh knowledge and tackling unfamiliar tasks in an original and innovative manner.
- *Social aging* – is concerned with the roles you choose to play, or are compelled to adopt by family and friends or society at large, the expectations such roles create in yourself and others and the rewards they offer. It has to do with society's attitude towards you, your personal feelings about growing chronologically older and the way in which you react to changing situations.

One birthday – many ages
Far from being a single process measured against the calender, therefore, aging is the outcome of a continual, complex and dynamic interaction of biological, psychological, intellectual and social factors which between them determine your system's rate of regeneration and degeneration.

In this and the following chapter we shall be exploring these four factors, starting with biological aging. Depending, largely, on the lifestyle you have adopted, these ages may be greater or lower than your chronological age. Where the results indicate that you are older than your age in birthdays, it means that your way of living is promoting system degeneration while inhibiting regeneration. When your assessed age with regard to any of the four factors is less than your chronological age, the opposite holds true. You will be using these findings in order to develop a FAR programme personally tailored to meet your unique, individual needs.

When completing the questionnaires, I suggest that you jot down your responses on a sheet of paper rather than marking the book, since you will want to repeat the analysis on future occasions in order to discover the extent to which the FAR programme is enhancing your health and longevity. Simply note which of the answers best reflects your current condition or habits.

Assessment One – Biological aging

1 To perform this simple test, strip to the waist and pinch up a fold of skin, between thumb and finger, at a spot just below the waist and immediately above the hip bone. Estimate its thickness. As women naturally have more subcutaneous fat than men, you must be careful to score for the appropriate section below:

Men **a**: less than ½″, **b**: ½″–1″, **c**: 1″–2″, **d**: 2″+
Women **a**: less than 1″, **b**: 1″–2″, **c**: 2″–3″, **d**: 3″+

2 Accurately measure your girth at waist and hips. Compare the two:

a: waist measures less than hips measure, **b**: both within ½″ of one another, **c**: waist greater than hips by 1″, **d**: waist greater by more than 1″.

3 The next check involves some simple arithmetic in calculating your ideal weight.

Men: Multiply your height in inches by 4, then take away

128. For example, if you are 5′ 8″ tall, the calculation is: ideal weight = (68 × 4) − 128 = 144 lbs, or 10st. 3lbs. *Women*: Multiply your height in inches by 3.5 and then subtract 108. A woman 5′ 4″ tall would calculate as follows: ideal weight = (64 × 3.5) − 108 = 116lbs = 8st. 3lbs.

If you are one of those many people for whom even the simplest of sums evokes blind terror, take your ideal weight from the table in the Appendix. But, since this table only includes a limited range of heights and weights, you will get a slightly more accurate result by carrying out the calculation.

This calculation is most accurate if you have a fairly average build. People with a very large or rather smaller than usual frame will find it more satisfactory to calculate their body mass index, using the method given on p. 48. Having calculated your ideal weight, use the following ratings:

a: ideal weight within 3lbs of actual weight, **b**: ideal weight plus or minus 7lbs, **c**: ideal weight plus or minus 8–14lbs, **d**: more than 14lbs above or below ideal weight

4 We now consider how much exercise you take each week. This must be sufficiently hard, and last long enough, to increase your pulse rate for twenty minutes. Exercise which should do this includes brisk walking, jogging, running, cycling, swimming – provided it is continuous and vigorous – squash or tennis. Excluded are such sports as weight-training and golf. Sessions are over a one-week period.

a: six or more sessions per week, **b**: between three and five, **c**: between one and two, **d**: less than once a week

5 Now we turn from exercise to eating habits, since diet – not surprisingly – plays a major role in determining the R:D balance.

The first statement concerns your consumption of saturated fats and cholesterol. If you have been given information about your cholesterol level during a recent (within the past six months) medical check and your lifestyle has not changed significantly since that time, use the first series

of ratings to score this statement. If you do not know your
cholesterol level, then refer to the notes on diet below. But
read the section on cholesterol on pp. 49–50 in order to put
yourself more fully in the picture about any risks you run.

If your cholesterol level is known:

a: less than 150, **b**: 150–79, **c**: 180–99, **d**: 200–40, **e**: 241 or
more (Milligrams per 100 ml)

If your cholesterol level is not known, consider your diet
over a typical week, awarding +1 point for each of the
foods listed below if eaten as indicated.

Food	Quantity per day
Eggs	Two or more
Cheese (except low fat)	More than 5 oz
Milk (excluding skimmed)	More than two pints
Cream	Any amount
Red meat	More than 10 oz
Brains, liver, kidneys	More than 8 oz
	Quantity per week
Fried foods (excluding vegetables)	More than twice
Chips	More than twice
Shellfish	More than once
Chocolate	More than 2 oz

Award your rating on this statement according to the
number of points totalled:

a: 0–3, **b**: 4–6, **c**: 7–9, **d**: 10–15, **e**: +15

6 How much salt do you eat?

a: none added to food, no convenience foods eaten,
b: occasional (i.e. no more than twice a week) high-salt foods;
salt not added at table, **c**: salt used in cooking and at table,
d: salt frequently added at table, **e**: regular consumption of
high-salt foods

7 What is your carbohydrate consumption?

Score this part of the questionnaire by estimating how many portions you eat on an average day. A portion consists of the following amounts:

Sweets, chocolates, jam, honey (1oz)
Sugar in drinks, i.e. tea or coffee (one teaspoon)
Soft drinks (except slimline drinks) (one glass)
Cakes, puddings, biscuits (one helping)
Breakfast cereals with sugar (one serving)
Canned vegetables (one serving)

a: 0–1, **b**: 2–3, **c**: 4–5, **d**: 6–7, **e**: more than 7

8 How much alcohol do you drink?
Consumption of alcohol is measured in standard units. One unit = half a pint of beer, lager, cider etc.; one glass of wine, sherry or vermouth; one measure (⅕ gill) spirits. For instance, if you drink three pints of beer you will have consumed 6 standard units. Total your average consumption *in units* per day.

If male score as follows: **a**: 0–3, **b**: 4–5, **c**: 6–7, **d**: more than 7
If female score as follows: **a**: 0–2, **b**: 3–4, **c**: 5–6, **d**: more than 6

9 How about fresh fruit, vegetables, pulses and wholemeal bread? Award yourself 1 point for every portion consumed during an average week. A portion consists of the following amounts:

Fresh fruit (one item)
Fresh (raw) vegetables (8 oz)
Bran, pulses and other high-roughage foods (4 oz)
Wholemeal bread (one slice)

a: more than 10 points, **b**: 7–9, **c**: 4–6, **d**: less than 4

10 Have you had a medical check-up which passed you as fit in: **a**: the last six months, **b**: the last twelve months, **c**: the last two years, **d**: more than that time or never? If you have had a recent examination in which you were told that there was a serious medical problem, such as a serious heart murmur, an ulcer or diabetes, score this as **d**.

11 Have you been for a dental check in: **a**: the last six months, **b**: the last twelve months, **c**: the last two years, **d**: or is it more than two years since you last saw your dentist?

12 What was your blood pressure on the last check-up?

If you don't know your blood pressure score this as **a**. When the doctor or nurse takes your blood pressure, two measures are obtained. I shall be explaining what these mean later in this chapter. For the moment you need consider only the higher of the two figures you were given. Called systolic pressure, it is a reflection of your heart's pumping efficiency.

b: 110–120, **c**: 121–130, **d**: 131–49, **e**: 150–70, **f**: 171–89, **g**: more than 190

13 Now for something over which we have no control, although it plays an important role in longevity. This is the health record and age of your parents, which are analysed in the next three questions. If they are dead, then you should choose the statement for the age at which death occurred.

a: no history of heart disease in my family, **b**: one relative over 60 with heart trouble, **c**: two relatives over 60 with heart trouble, **d**: one relative under 60 with heart trouble, **e**: two relatives under 60 with heart trouble

14

a: father alive and under 68 years, **b**: alive, or died, aged 69–73, **c**: alive, or died, aged 74–80, **d**: alive, or died, aged 85+, **e**: died of medical causes (not an accident) before the age of 68

15

a: mother alive and under 73, **b**: alive, or died, aged 74–80, **c**: alive, or died, aged 81–90, **d**: alive, or died, aged 90+, **e**: died of medical causes (not an accident) before the age of 73

16 Vitamin and mineral supplements.

If you don't take any score this as **a**. If you take any additional vitamins or minerals, on a regular basis and at least five times per week, then award yourself 1 point for each of the following taken, whether on its own or as part of a multi-vitamin or multi-mineral preparation (check the container if you are not certain just what the pills contain): vitamin C, vitamin E, thiamine (B1), riboflavin (B2), niacin (niacinamide, nicotinic acid) (B3), pantothenic acid (B5), pyridoxine (pyridoxol, pyridoxamine) (B6), cobalamins (B12), folic acid (folacin), biotin, choline, inositol, lecithin, PABA (para-amino-benzoic-acid), iodine, magnesium, calcium, phosphorous, iron, zinc, copper, potassium, manganese, selenium, chromium, molybdenum.

b: more than 20 points, **c**: 15–19 points, **d**: 6–14 points, **e**: less than 6 points

17 General health.

Award yourself 1 point for each of the conditions below, if you have suffered from them on more than four occasions during the past six months: bad dandruff, recurrent mouth ulcers, coated or smooth sore tongue, indigestion or heartburn, migraine or serious non-migraine headache, large areas of acne, dry skin, sudden increase in hair loss, more than two head colds, lingering catarrh, painful sinuses, sore throat, constipation, cracking at corners of mouth, bruised or enlarged veins under tongue, dry cracked lips, brittle or split nails.

a: 8+, **b**: 5–7, **c**: 2–4, **d**: 1 or none

18 Do you work in conditions which are unusually noisy, dusty, dirty, humid or hot?

a: rarely or never, **b**: between 2 and 6 hours per week, **c**: between 7 and 20 hours per week, **d**: more than 20 hours per week

19 If you are a non-smoker award yourself an **a**. If you smoke score as follows: **b**: up to 10 cigarettes per day, **c**: 10– 30 per day, **d**: 31–40 per day, **e**: more than 40 per day. If you smoke a pipe each day or two cigars a week per week, score **b**. If you smoke more than two cigars per week score **c**.

20 Do you find it easy to unwind and relax at the end of a hard day?

  a: strongly agree, **b**: agree to some extent, **c**: disagree,
  d: strongly disagree.

That concludes your first FAR assessment, which investigated your biological age. Score by awarding points according to the chart below. Then use the figures in Table 2 on p. 46 to discover what the result reveals about your biological age.

Score chart for Assessment One

```
 1   a -5   b +1   c +3   d +5
 2   a -5   b +2   c +3   d +5
 3   a -5   b +1   c +3   d +5
 4   a -5   b -3   c +2   d +5
 5   a -5   b -2   c +2   d +3   e +5
 6   a -5   b -2   c +2   d +3   e +5
 7   a -5   b -2   c +2   d +3   e +5
 8   a -5   b +2   c +3   d +5
 9   a -5   b -3   c -1   d +5
10   a -5   b +1   c +2   d +5
11   a -5   b -3   c +3   d +5
12   a +3   b -5   c -1   d  0   e +1   f If male +3;
                                        if female +4   g +5
13   a -5   b +1   c +2   d +3   e +5
14   a  0   b -1   c -2   d -5   e +5
15   a  0   b -2   c -3   d -5   e +5
16   a +5   b -5   c -3   d -2   e -1
17   a +5   b +3   c +1   d -5
18   a -5   b +1   c +3   d +5
19   a -5   b +1   c +2   d +3   e +5
20   a -5   b -3   c +3   d +5
```

Total your scores carefully, taking into account the (+) or (−) signs.

Total score on Assessment One = -29 (0 : -40)

To convert this result into a factor indicating your biological age, refer to Table 2. You'll be using the same table to discover your aging factor from each of the assessment scores. It is essential to take positive and negative scores into account when adding your score, since the final result determines whether the factor should be added to your chronological age or subtracted from it.

If your assessment score is *positive* you *add* the factor obtained from the table to your chronological age. This suggests that degeneration is occurring more rapidly than regeneration.

If your assessment score is *negative* then you must *subtract* the figure taken from the table from your age in years. A negative assessment score suggests that your current lifestyle is enhancing regeneration. This means that you are biologically younger than your birthdays suggest.

How to use the table

Locate the aging factor associated with your age and your assessment score. If you are aged 25, 35, 45, 55, 65 or 75 adopt the following procedure for determining the appropriate age range. When there are 6 months or more to your next birthday, use your current age – i.e. 35 years and 5 months puts you in the 26–35 age range. If there are less than 6 months to your next birthday, then move to the next age range – i.e. 35 years and 7 months places you in the 36–45 range.

If you scored less than 10 on the assessment, whether the total was positive or negative, there is no need to refer to the table since such a low total suggests that your biological (or psychological/intellectual/social) age and chronological age are identical.

Do not worry if this looks a little complicated at first. It is quick and easy to use, as a couple of examples will prove.

Suppose your score is +38 and your chronological age is 47. From the table you obtain an aging factor of 9 which, because your total score on the assessment was positive, must be added to your age in years: 47 + 9 = 56 years. In other words your current lifestyle appears to be aging your body to the point where it is the biological equivalent of that of a person in their mid-fifties.

Table 2

Age	Assessment Score					
	100–80	**79–60**	**59–40**	**39–25**	**24–16**	**15–10**
20–25	5	4	3	2	1	1
26–35	8	7	6	5	4	3
36–45	12	10	8	7	6	5
46–55	15	12	10	9	7	6
56–65	25	20	15	12	10	8
66–75	20	18	12	10	8	6
75+	15	12	10	6	5	4

If however, your total score on the assessment had been −38, that same factor would have been subtracted from your chronological age to give 47 − 9 = 38 as your biological age. In this case your body is younger than the number of birthdays you have celebrated would indicate.

Here's a second example, this time involving an assessment score of −62, achieved by a 55-year-old. From the table we find that the aging factor in this case is 12. Since the assessment score is negative, this has to be taken away from chronological age, giving a biological age of 55 − 12 = 43 years.

Had the assessment score been positive, the same value would have been added to the chronological age, giving a total biological age of 67.

Where a positive score is obtained, you must work to reduce the degree of degeneration which is occurring by means of the FAR procedures. Where the score is negative, you can enhance regeneration still further by adopting the programme.

The distribution of age factors in the table reflects the fact that least damage, and fewest gains, occur during the first three, and final few, decades of life. Up to the age of thirty, the system is maximally resistant to degeneration because natural regeneration is powerful enough to counter many of the adverse effects of lifestyle.

After sixty, if the system has degenerated to any significant extent, recovery – although not impossible – is far harder and the likely gains more limited. Equally, a body which is in good shape at sixty is less likely to degenerate much faster during the next couple of decades provided the same, regeneration-enhancing, lifestyle continues to be followed.

At either end of the age range, however, the effort and energy invested in FAR procedures are certainly not going to be wasted. During young adulthood they help to create the firm foundations of physical health, fitness and stamina essential for a healthy longevity. And during late adulthood following the FAR programme can help sustain fitness, regain lost vitality and help prevent many of the commonly experienced health problems.

It should also be noted that any regeneration indicated by a negative score on the assessment represents only that degree of enhancement one normally expects to find in somebody following a sensible lifestyle, i.e. taking exercise, eating properly and avoiding hazardous surroundings. While all these are featured in the FAR programme, its active regenerative procedures mean that far greater gains can be expected at all ages. Indeed it should be possible significantly to increase the figures given.

Why the statements were selected

Although the reasons behind some of the statements, or questions, are best left to a full explanation in later chapters, it will be helpful to consider the relevance of the others selected for inclusion in this chapter.

3 *Body weight*

You may wonder why I didn't spare you the arithmetic by simply using one of those height/weight charts you find in virtually every book on health and fitness. The problem is that, although convenient, studies suggest that they are not all that reliable. Based on insurance companies' analysis of which of their policy-holders live longest, the first such chart was published in 1959 and revised in 1983 to take account of changes in the mortality statistics. These changes can make a significant difference to the results.

On the first chart, produced by the Metropolitan Life Insurance Company, for example, the weight range for a 5' 6" tall woman was 115–47lbs, while a man of that height was expected to weigh between 123–56lbs. The 1983 revision gave the ideal weights for that height as between 120–60lbs for women and 133–63lbs for men.

But many experts are not happy with either version, considering the first too conservative and the second too generous. If you'd like a more precise indication of your weight/height combination, and aren't daunted by a little arithmetic – which is easy to perform using a calculator – you may be interested in calculating something known as the body mass index or BMI. Specialists at the US National Institute of Aging regard BMI as an especially accurate way of determining whether a person is overweight for their height. Here's how to do it:

Multiply your weight in pounds by 703. Divide the result by your height in inches. Repeat the division by height. This gives your BMI.

An example will help make this clear. Suppose you are 68 inches tall and weigh 165lbs. The BMI calculation is as follows: $165 \times 703 = 115,995$. Dividing by a height of 68 inches gives us $115,995/68 = 1705.8$. The second division by the height produces $1705.8/68 = 25.1$.

A BMI of 20–25 is regarded as normal and, should you wish to check it against your original response to statement **3**, a score in the normal range receives an **a**. A BMI between 26 and 30 is a **b** while a BMI over 30 scores as **d**. This figure, which is achieved by 34 million Americans, is considered a sign of 'medically significant obesity'.

A second useful measure of obesity is the girth test (statement **1**). Studies have shown that carrying excess fat around the stomach, in the shape of a pot-belly, is more dangerous than having fatty legs or buttocks because the risk of heart disease rises significantly.

5 *Cholesterol*

Since 1984, and the publication of the results of a ten-year, $150-million study by the US National Heart, Lung and Blood Institute in Washington DC, there has not been the slightest doubt that a reduction in blood cholesterol substantially reduces the risk of heart attacks.

Technically, cholesterol is not a fat but an alcohol belonging to a group of substances called sterols. It is obtained from animal products in the diet, and manufactured by every organ in the body except the adult brain. Its main production site within the body is the liver, which can produce far more than we obtain from diet. A regulatory mechanism reduces liver production of cholesterol when the body's needs are being satisfied through nutrition.

Cholesterol is essential to life. Not only is it used to form cell-wall membrane, it is also present in hormones and bile salt. Unfortunately it is also a significant factor in heart disease, forming the wax-like substance which coats and thickens the artery walls.

But it's not just a case of 'the less cholesterol the better'. Cholesterol is transported around the body with other substances – proteins and triglycerides – in a combination called a lipoprotein. These come in four categories, depending on the relative proportions of the different substances which comprise them.

Of most importance to this discussion is low-density lipoprotein (LDL), which is the main carrier of cholesterol in the bloodstream, and high-density lipoprotein (HDL), which carries very little and performs a vital protective function. While most attention was previously paid to LDL, because of the amount of cholesterol it carries, researchers now consider that HDL levels are even more significant in preventing heart disease.

It is known that women have higher levels of HDL than men, which may help explain why their incidence of heart disease is, on average, six times lower than that of men. Furthermore, obesity, diabetes and chronic renal disease all involve a higher risk of heart disease, while being associated with lowered HDL levels.

Exercise increases the level of HDL, which may be one of

its most crucial functions in preventing heart disease. So too do moderate amounts of alcohol. This is why a low level of consumption received a negative score in statement **8**. In excess, of course, drinking leads to other forms of disease and cellular degeneration.

The diet and exercise procedures in your FAR programme will help to increase HDL levels, while preventing excess amounts of total cholesterol from occurring.

7 *Carbohydrates*
It is important to distinguish between refined carbohydrates, especially white sugar, found in most processed and manufactured foods and the unrefined carbohydrates present in brown rice, fresh fruit, vegetables, pasta and wholemeal bread. The former accelerate degenerative changes while the latter are either neutral or enhance regeneration.

The significance of carbohydrates in the diet will be discussed in later chapters.

12 *Blood pressure*
When you have your blood pressure taken, two measures are obtained; the upper one for systolic pressure and the lower for diastolic pressure. Systolic pressure refers to the power of your heart's pumping action, while diastolic pressure is that measured during the resting period between pulses.

Blood pressure is normally measured in millimetres of mercury, whose chemical symbol is Hg. The World Health Organisation has defined normal (normotension) blood pressure as a systolic reading below 140mm Hg and a diastolic reading below 90mm Hg. In the West average blood pressure is 120 – 80mm Hg. The conditions under which blood pressure is taken are important, since not only does it vary over the twenty-four-hour period but is markedly affected by such things as stress, eating, exercise and so on. Even the anxiety of having your blood pressure taken can lead to an increase. Although it is widely believed that high blood pressure is associated with headaches, dizziness, fatigue and lethargy, these symptoms are an unreliable indicator since you are just as likely to find them among people whose blood pressure is normal as among hypertension sufferers.

Indeed you can be seriously hypertensive, with a *diastolic* pressure of 115mm or higher, and show no symptoms at all. It is for this reason that having your blood pressure checked regularly is sound health practice, which is why not knowing your blood pressure gave a positive score.

In up to 95 per cent of cases, there is no identifiable cause of the hypertension, which is referred to as primary or 'essential'. In the remaining cases, the high blood pressure is secondary to some underlying problem, such as kidney disease. It is with helping to reduce 'essential' hypertension that the FAR programme is concerned.

There is reason to believe, for instance, that excess salt in the diet leads to raised blood pressure (it was for this reason that statement **6** was included). One way of reducing, or avoiding, hypertension could be to reduce salt intake. Other factors involved are obesity, cigarette-smoking, chronic stress, and drinking alcohol to excess – i.e. 37 or more standard units per week for men, and 25 or more for women. Increasing calcium and potassium will also help.

Untreated hypertension is very important to the FAR programme as prolonged high blood pressure presents a significant risk to health and longevity. Men with an elevated systolic pressure are twice as likely to die from heart disease as men with normal systolic pressure, even when their diastolic pressure is below the danger level. Hypertension can hasten death not only from heart failure and strokes, but by damaging the kidneys – whose effective function is critically dependent on blood pressure.

Data from one of the most extensive research projects into heart disease, known as the Framingham Study, have shown that the incidence of coronary heart disease increases by 20 per cent for every 10mm rise in systolic pressure. At 160mm Hg there is twice the risk found at 110mm Hg. A diastolic pressure of 110mm Hg during middle age leads to a one in five probability of death within five years if left untreated.

So the answer is to have your blood pressure checked

regularly by a doctor, and receive treatment if hypertensive.

There is, by the way, no risk associated with a low blood pressure unless you are also suffering from some other medical condition, such as a haemorrhage or burns. In fact a low blood pressure is beneficial to one's health and fitness.

19 *Smoking*

If you are a smoker, you are almost certainly sick to death of being told of the risks you run. The trouble is that 'sick to death' is exactly what cigarettes are likely to make you. Burning cigarettes produce around 4,000 chemical substances, although most of the attention has so far been focused on just two of them, nicotine and carbon monoxide.

It seems likely, however, that many of the other chemicals have an equally harmful effect on the body and may be responsible for the furring-up (atheroma) of the coronary arteries which leads to the high incidence of heart disease among smokers.

There is also evidence that smoking promotes the build-up of the fatty plaque which leads to thrombosis. In addition, there are the well-known hazards of cancer, bronchitis and emphysema. Men who smoke are slightly more at risk than women smokers, and run about twice the risk of non-smokers of acquiring these illnesses. The more you smoke, the greater the self-imposed dangers.

If you cannot stop smoking, then reduce the risk you run by switching to a low-tar, low-nicotine brand, by leaving a longer stub, by reducing the frequency and depth of inhalation and, perhaps, by giving up cigarettes in favour of a pipe. You should also cut down the number smoked each day by disciplining yourself not to smoke in certain situations, such as at home – where your family may be adversely affected by passive inhalation of your smoke.

Assessing your other invisible ages

For the next step of your FAR programme, you must evaluate your degree of psychological, intellectual and social aging. This can be done using the assessments provided in the next chapter.

Four: Assessing your invisible aging

'We are thinking beings, and we cannot
exclude the intellect from participating in any
of our functions.'

(William James – *Varieties of Religious
Experience*)

For centuries physicians have recognised the powerful influence which mind can exert over bodily functioning.
There is a wide range of physical symptoms – ranging from
tics and tremors to flatulence, vomiting, paralysis and even
the loss of sight or hearing – which occur only because the
mind wills them into being. Known as conversion
hysterias, they are seen as the bodily expression of a
psychic conflict. Even more frequently, one encounters
psychogenic illnesses where health is threatened by disorders which, although undoubtedly of an organic,
physical nature are strongly influenced by psychosocial and
emotional factors. Examples include asthma, peptic ulcers,
migraines, colitis, hypertension, menstrual disorders,
sexual dysfunction, such skin diseases as eczema and
psoriasis, and many others. Most of us have personal experience of the effects of emotional or other psychological
problems on our resistance to infections. While going
through a difficult time with our partner or during a period
of chronic stress at work, we seem to go down with far
more colds, throat infections or flu. And if the distress is
sufficiently acute we may develop shingles as our now less
efficient immune system fails to prevent the herpes virus
from multiplying.

Psychological, intellectual and social factors can cause us
to age from the inside out. Over the past years, I have had
many clients whose youthful appearance belied the true
extent to which their systems had invisibly aged in terms of
their psychological and intellectual functioning.

James was a youthful-looking bank official who consulted me for depression, general anxiety and worries about his inability to meet the intellectual demands of a new post. Aged thirty-three, he was both psychologically and intellectually nearly a decade older. His approach to life was excessively cautious and inflexible. He feared change and saw any unfamiliar challenges as threats to be avoided. James found it hard to make friends, and impossible to sustain a lasting personal relationship. These attitudes and anxieties had severely limited his professional and private life. His outlook was narrow and he was entirely lacking in enthusiasm or interest.

These were not, however, merely symptoms of his depression. Even before he had become depressed, it was clear that James had long viewed life in a negative manner.

James's invisible aging was all the more incongruous because of his youthful, almost baby-faced appearance and excellent physical fitness. He swam, played squash, was sensible about his diet and achieved a negative score of 81 on the first assessment, giving him a biological age of twenty-five. His body reminded one of a healthy young adult at the peak of his regenerative potency. His intellectual and emotional status, however, was that of a middle-aged man in whom degeneration is triumphing.

In this chapter, you will be exploring your own degree of invisible aging – the greying that, although it takes place out of sight inside the mind, can still exert a powerful influence on the rate and extent of physical degeneration.

Assessment Two – Psychological aging

This questionnaire is to be answered as before, by noting any response which best reflects your own feelings or behaviour, either now or at any time over the past six months.

Once again it is advisable to record your answers on a separate sheet of paper, rather than marking the book, since you will be reassessing your psychological, intellectual and social ages on future occasions while working with the FAR programme.

1 I wake early and then sleep poorly for the rest of the night: **a**:regularly, **b**:frequently, **c**:occasionally, **d**:rarely or never.

2 I look forward to the start of each new day: **a**: regularly, **b**:frequently, **c**:occasionally, **d**:rarely or never.

3 I feel anxious without any good reason: **a**:regularly, **b**:frequently, **c**:occasionally, **d**:rarely or never.

4 I am confident of my ability to cope with life's challenges: **a**:strongly agree, **b**:agree to some extent, **c**:disagree, **d**:strongly disagree.

5 I feel blue for no apparent reason: **a**:regularly, **b**:frequently, **c**:occasionally, **d**:rarely or never.

6 There is at least one other person in whom I feel able to confide my worries, fears, hopes and joys: **a**:true at the present time, **b**:true to some extent at the present time, **c**:not true at the present time, **d**:has not been true for many years.

7 I feel sexually frustrated: **a**:rarely or never, **b**:occasionally, **c**:frequently, **d**:much of the time.

8 I have at least one close and loving relationship in my life: **a**:very true, **b**:true to some extent, **c**:not true at present, **d**:not true and has not been so for many years.

9 I find it easy to tell someone I am close to how much I love them: **a**:strongly agree, **b**:agree to some extent, **c**:disagree, **d**:strongly disagree.

10 I lose my temper over minor matters: **a**:regularly, **b**:frequently, **c**:occasionally, **d**:rarely or never.

11 I have no difficulty in standing up for my rights: **a**:strongly agree, **b**:agree to some extent, **c**:disagree, **d**:strongly disagree.

12 I feel guilty about past mistakes: **a**:very true, **b**:true to some extent, **c**:not true at present, **d**:has not been true for many years.

13 I lead a full and enjoyable social life: **a**:strongly agree, **b**:agree to some extent, **c**:disagree, **d**:strongly disagree.

14 I feel unable to exert as much control as I would like over the things which happen to me: **a**:strongly agree, **b**:agree to some extent, **c**:disagree, **d**:strongly disagree.

15 I frequently hide my emotions: **a**:strongly agree, **b**:agree to some extent, **c**:disagree, **d**:strongly disagree.

16 I have somebody with whom I would not feel embarrassed to share my innermost secrets: **a**:very true, **b**:true to some extent, **c**:not true at all at present, **d**:has not been true for many years.

17 I consider my life fulfilling: **a**:strongly agree, **b**:agree to some extent, **c**:disagree, **d**:strongly disagree.

18 I make new friends easily: **a**:strongly agree, **b**:agree to some extent, **c**:disagree, **d**:strongly disagree.

19 I face major changes in my life with confidence: **a**:strongly agree, **b**:agree to some extent, **c**:disagree, **d**:strongly disagree.

20 I have a partner and/or close friends in whom I have complete trust: **a**:strongly agree, **b**:agree to some extent, **c**:disagree, **d**:strongly disagree.

Score chart for Assessment Two
Use exactly the same procedure as before, awarding points according to the rating selected. Remember to take account of positive and negative scores so as to arrive at a single result which is either a + or − number.

	a	b	c	d
1	+5	+3	+1	−5
2	−5	−3	−1	+5
3	+5	+2	+1	−5
4	−5	−3	+2	+5
5	+5	+3	+1	−5
6	−5	−3	+3	+5
7	−5	−3	+3	+5
8	−5	−3	+3	+5
9	−5	−2	+3	+5
10	+5	+3	−5	−3
11	−5	−3	+3	+5
12	+5	+3	−3	−5
13	−5	−2	+3	+5
14	+5	+3	−3	−5
15	+5	+3	−5	−3
16	−5	−3	+3	+5
17	−5	−3	+3	+5
18	−5	−3	+3	+5
19	−5	−3	+3	+5
20	−5	−3	+3	+5

Total score on Assessment Two =   -38   (0 : -42)

To convert this score into your psychological age, refer to Table 2 on p. 46 and use it in exactly the same way as when identifying your biological aging factor. Remember that a negative total score on the assessment means that you subtract the factor given in the table from your chronological age, while a positive final total means that the aging factor has to be added.

Assessment Three – Intellectual aging

1 My work is tedious, routine and undemanding: **a**:regularly, **b**:frequently, **c**:occasionally, **d**:rarely or never.

2 My work presents me with a constant flow of fresh intellectual challenges: **a**:regularly, **b**:frequently, **c**:occasionally, **d**:rarely or never.

3 I enjoy leisure activities which make demands on my mind, such as playing chess, doing crosswords, brain teasers etc.: **a**:regularly, **b**:frequently, **c**:occasionally, **d**:rarely or never.

4 I attend evening classes or follow a course of mentally demanding training at home: **a**:on a regular basis, **b**:frequently, **c**:occasionally, **d**:not at all in the past two years.

5 I read serious fiction or non-fiction books: **a**:regularly, **b**:frequently, **c**:occasionally, **d**:rarely or never.

6 I worry that my memory is getting worse as I get older: **a**:strongly agree, **b**:agree to some extent, **c**:disagree, **d**:strongly disagree.

7 I find myself delaying important decisions because of anxiety about making a bad choice: **a**:strongly agree, **b**:agree to some extent, **c**:disagree, **d**:strongly disagree.

8 I become anxious when confronted by unfamiliar technical equipment: **a**:strongly agree, **b**:agree to some extent, **c**:disagree, **d**:strongly disagree.

9 I feel in complete control of my workload: **a**:regularly, **b**:frequently, **c**:occasionally, **d**:rarely or never.

10 I devote time to a creative leisure activity, such as painting, pottery, drama, writing, model-making etc.: **a**:regularly, **b**:frequently, **c**:occasionally, **d**:rarely or never.

11 If I fail to solve an intellectually demanding problem I

assume it's a result of lack of intelligence on my part:
a:strongly agree, **b**:agree to some extent, **c**:disagree,
d:strongly disagree.

12 I memorise poetry or prose passages for my own entertainment: **a**:regularly, **b**:frequently, **c**:occasionally,
d:rarely or never.

13 I am willing to trust my own judgement even when
others claim I am wrong: **a**:strongly agree, **b**:agree to some
extent, **c**:disagree, **d**:strongly disagree.

14 I love constant change and variety: **a**:strongly agree,
b:agree to some extent, **c**:disagree, **d**:strongly disagree.

15 As one grows older the brain starts working far less
efficiently: **a**:strongly agree, **b**:agree to some extent,
c:disagree, **d**:strongly disagree.

16 I am confident of my ability to learn new skills or
acquire fresh knowledge at any age: **a**:strongly agree,
b:agree to some extent, **c**:disagree, **d**:strongly disagree.

17 I keep up-to-date with the latest developments in arts
and science: **a**:regularly, **b**:frequently, **c**:occasionally,
d:rarely or never.

18 I have a vivid imagination which I use regularly:
a:strongly agree, **b**:agree to some extent, **c**:disagree,
d:strongly disagree.

19 I keep myself well informed about current affairs:
a:strongly agree, **b**:agree to some extent, **c**:disagree,
d:strongly disagree.

20 I am confronted by a wide range of different problems
in my working life: **a**:regularly, **b**:frequently, **c**:occasionally,
d:rarely or never.

Score chart for Assessment Three

1	**a** +5	**b** +3	**c** +2	**d** −5
2	**a** −5	**b** −3	**c** +3	**d** +5
3	**a** −5	**b** −3	**c** +3	**d** +5
4	**a** −5	**b** −2	**c** +3	**d** +5
5	**a** −5	**b** −3	**c** +3	**d** +5
6	**a** +5	**b** +3	**c** −2	**d** −5
7	**a** +5	**b** +3	**c** +2	**d** −5
8	**a** +5	**b** +3	**c** −2	**d** −5
9	**a** −5	**b** −3	**c** +2	**d** +5

10	a −5	b −3	c −2	d +5
11	a +5	b +3	c −2	d −5
12	a −5	b −3	c −2	d +5
13	a −5	b −2	c +3	d +5
14	a −5	b −2	c +3	d +5
15	a +5	b +3	c −2	d −5
16	a −5	b −3	c +3	d +5
17	a −5	b −3	c −2	d +5
18	a −5	b −3	c +3	d +5
19	a −5	b −3	c +3	d +5
20	a −5	b −3	c −2	d +5

Total score on Assessment Three = −21 (0 ', +43)

As before, the result indicates the extent to which your current lifestyle is either promoting or inhibiting intellectual aging. Identify the factor involved from Table 2 on p. 46.

If the assessment scores show that your psychological and/or intellectual ages are less than your chronological age, this does not mean you are less mature or intelligent than someone of the same physical age. It merely indicates that you are inhibiting these key aspects of degeneration by following a regeneration-enhancing lifestyle.

The final assessment explores the extent of your social aging.

Assessment Four – Social aging

1 My life was far more enjoyable when I was young: **a**:strongly agree, **b**:agree to some extent, **c**:disagree, **d**:strongly disagree.

2 I feel agreeably challenged and stimulated by the pace of modern life: **a**:regularly, **b**:frequently, **c**:occasionally, **d**:rarely or never.

3 I often yearn for the slower pace of days gone by: **a**:strongly agree, **b**:agree to some extent, **c**:disagree, **d**:strongly disagree.

4 I spend a lot of time these days reflecting on the past: **a**:strongly agree, **b**:agree to some extent, **c**:disagree, **d**:strongly disagree.

5 The prospect of growing old greatly depresses me: **a**:strongly agree, **b**:agree to some extent, **c**:disagree, **d**:strongly disagree.

6 I can usually get along with people of all ages: **a**:strongly agree, **b**:agree to some extent, **c**:disagree, **d**:strongly disagree.

7 I am a great respecter of tradition: **a**:strongly agree, **b**:agree to some extent, **c**:disagree, **d**:strongly disagree.

8 I always obey rules and regulations: **a**:strongly agree, **b**:agree to some extent, **c**:disagree, **d**:strongly disagree.

9 I feel anxious when thinking about my future: **a**:strongly agree, **b**:agree to some extent, **c**:disagree, **d**:strongly disagree.

10 I feel threatened by younger people: **a**:strongly agree, **b**:agree to some extent, **c**:disagree, **d**:strongly disagree.

11 I resent not having received sufficient recognition for my achievements in life: **a**:strongly agree, **b**:agree to some extent, **c**:disagree, **d**:strongly disagree.

12 I often regret missed opportunities in life: **a**:strongly agree, **b**:agree to some extent, **c**:disagree, **d**:strongly disagree.

13 I do not easily forgive and forget those who have dealt unfairly with me: **a**:strongly agree, **b**:agree to some extent, **c**:disagree, **d**:strongly disagree.

14 I am dreading having to retire (or the time when my partner has to retire): **a**:strongly agree, **b**:agree to some extent, **c**:disagree, **d**:strongly disagree.

15 I dislike most modern art: **a**:strongly agree, **b**:agree to some extent, **c**:disagree, **d**:strongly disagree.

16 Some popular music has great artistic merit: **a**:strongly agree, **b**:agree to some extent, **c**:disagree, **d**:strongly disagree.

17 I lie about my age: **a**:regularly, **b**:frequently, **c**:occasionally, **d**:rarely or never.

18 I envy those younger than myself: **a**:strongly agree, **b**:agree to some extent, **c**:disagree, **d**:strongly disagree.

19 I disapprove of people having partners much younger than they are: **a**:strongly agree, **b**:agree to some extent, **c**:disagree, **d**:strongly disagree.

20 I feel as fit and confident now as I did ten years ago:

a:strongly agree, **b**:agree to some extent, **c**:disagree, **d**:strongly disagree.

Score chart for Assessment Four
As before, total the + and − numbers carefully to produce a single score for this assessment, then refer to Table 2 on p. 46 to identify your aging factor.

1	a +5	b +2	c −3	d −5
2	a −5	b −4	c −1	d +5
3	a +5	b +2	c −2	d −5
4	a +5	b +3	c −2	d −5
5	a +5	b +3	c −2	d −5
6	a −5	b −2	c +2	d +5
7	a +5	b +3	c −2	d −5
8	a +5	b +3	c −2	d −5
9	a +5	b +3	c −3	d −5
10	a +5	b +3	c −3	d −5
11	a +5	b +3	c −2	d −5
12	a +5	b +3	c −3	d −5
13	a +5	b +3	c −3	d −5
14	a +5	b +3	c −3	d −5
15	a +5	b +3	c −2	d −5
16	a −5	b −3	c +3	d +5
17	a +5	b +3	c −2	d −5
18	a +5	b +3	c −3	d −5
19	a +5	b +3	c −3	d −5
20	a −5	b −3	c +2	d +5

Total score on Assessment Four = −43 (0 : −45)

Assessing overall aging
Results from the four assessments will also provide an indication of your overall rate of aging as shown by the Regeneration:Degeneration balance.

Add together your four scores, once again taking account of positive and negative results when reaching your overall total.

Suppose, for instance, that somebody aged thirty-five

obtained the following scores: Assessment One = −60; Assessment Two = −50; Assessment Three = +50; Assessment Four = −40. Here we get −150 plus +50, giving us a total of −100. Using Table 3, below, we find that this score is equal to an aging factor of 8 for someone aged thirty-five. As the total score was negative this must, as before, be subtracted from the chronological age, giving an overall age of twenty-seven.

Table 3

Age	Over 300	299–250	249–100	99–40
		Score range for overall age		
20–30	8	7	6	5
31–40	10	9	8	7
41–50	15	12	10	9
51–60	25	15	12	11
61–70	20	18	15	12
71+	15	12	10	9

My overall age = 27   (0 = 34)

Using your assessment results
I suggest that you make a written record of these results, in order to keep track of your progress over the next few months while following the FAR programme.

Even if you obtained a high negative score on all four assessments, there is very likely to be some scope for improvement. By adopting the procedures described in the remainder of the book you should be able to tilt the R:D balance even more firmly in your favour. Pay special attention to those aspects of your current lifestyle reflected in the statements on which you scored +5, since these are aging you more rapidly than is necessary. I suggest that you circle the relevant statement numbers on your record form. This assists in creating a FAR programme tailored to your individual requirements. Either copy, or photocopy, the record form below.

FAR record form

DATE OF FIRST ASSESSMENTS:

CHRONOLOGICAL AGE:

BIOLOGICAL AGE:

PSYCHOLOGICAL AGE:

INTELLECTUAL AGE:

SOCIAL AGE:

OVERALL AGE:

Statements with high positive score

Biological aging:
1 2 3 4 5 6 7 8 9 10 11 12 13 14 15 16 17 18 19 20

Psychological aging:
1 2 3 4 5 6 7 8 9 10 11 12 13 14 15 16 17 18 19 20

Intellectual aging:
1 2 3 4 5 6 7 8 9 10 11 12 13 14 15 16 17 18 19 20

Social aging:
1 2 3 4 5 6 7 8 9 10 11 12 13 14 15 16 17 18 19 20

About the assessments

These methods of calculating aging are, of course, only approximate. It is not yet possible precisely to determine the effects of each factor on the system as a whole. The assessments are designed to provide you with a guide as to the likely effects of your current lifestyle on aging rates both visible and invisible.

The essential thing to notice is the level of your scores and whether they are positive or negative.

Where a high positive score (more than +80) has

resulted, make a note of all those statements on which you scored the maximum of +5. When creating your FAR programme, include procedures which will reduce these values, or else make self-evident changes in your lifestyle that replace them with an equally high negative score.

Don't be deceived by appearances

Let's be clear that a high negative score, even on biological aging, doesn't necessarily mean that you'll look as young as the assessment results suggest you really are. There is no direct relationship between many of the outward signs we have come to associate with growing old – such as a certain type of hair loss, wrinkles or a greying head – and actual health or potential longevity.

While baldness, known medically as alopecia (from the Greek meaning 'fox-mange'), can result from chronic stress or a serious medical condition such as diabetes, there is also the characteristic loss due to a condition called male pattern baldness (MPB). This is determined by your body's genetically set clock and is not caused by accelerated biological or psychological degeneration. Even if hairs, complete with their follicles, are transplanted from a balding to a non-balding area of the scalp they will still drop out on schedule.

Similarly, a loss of skin elasticity and increased wrinkling is generally caused by exposure to the weather, especially ultra- violet light from the sun. While excessive sunshine – or light from a tanning bed – can be extremely hazardous, especially if you are light-skinned and unused to sunshine, small amounts of carefully regulated exposure from a UV-B tanning bed do little harm, especially during the winter months.

These external changes may accelerate social aging, if you allow others to pass judgements on you based solely on appearance, but they do not mean that you are as old as you look. Indeed, one of the fittest people I have ever met was a forty-year-old who, with weather-tanned features and a billiard-ball skull looked more like a man in his sixties. He had just finished sailing single-handed across the Atlantic when we met, and was planning to take his boat on a solo trip around the world. He achieved the highest ever negative scores on his FAR assessments and was in better regenerative shape than many people I have met in their twenties. So don't worry if you look older on the outside than you would wish. It's the extent of aging from inside out that counts when it comes to fitness, health and longevity.

The assessments in action.

To flesh out the bare, numerical, bones of the assessment scores, let's translate them into actual lifestyles. John and Mary, whose case history is described below, first came to see me five years ago after she became mildly agoraphobic. Their lifestyle is typical of many I have had described to me by couples in their early forties and illustrates the kind of problems identified by the assessments.

John and Mary met at university and married in their early twenties, soon after graduating. At that time he had just been appointed to a junior management position with a pharmaceutical company and she had started working as a teacher.

At that stage of their lives both were in excellent physical condition. John played a good game of squash, while Mary kept herself trim by regularly swimming and jogging. Both were ambitious, sociable and well liked by their wide and varied circle of friends, many of them made while at university.

By their early thirties they had a house, three children and a great deal of debt. The house was, and still is, on a substantial mortgage, they have a large bank overdraft and owe heavily on their credit cards. Many of their furnishings are on hire purchase.

John often lay awake at night worrying about the future, while Mary – who gave up her teaching career when their first child was born – began feeling bored and frustrated. She missed the stimulation of working outside the home, as well as the companionship. Their home was on a modern estate some distance from the nearby town centre. With only one car, which John needed for work, and public transport inconvenient and expensive, Mary found herself increasingly isolated. Her loneliness was accentuated by the long hours John felt obliged to work. Even at weekends he would shut himself away in his study, attending to reports and correspondence.

By their early forties John and Mary appeared, outwardly, an ideally happy couple with everything life has to offer – a delightful family, lovely home and secure future.

What was the truth? How were their lifestyles affecting the vital R:D balance?

John had given up playing squash several years earlier owing to pressure of work. Now his only exercise was to stroll around the houses with the dog, each evening, and play an occasional game of golf. He had developed a paunch, and his health had been further undermined by heavy smoking – he was on sixty a day – and regular social drinking.

His leisure interests – he once belonged to a French language society, played chess with his neighbour and attended regular courses at his local evening institute – had long been sacrificed to his ambitions at work. As a result his outlook was narrow and his views increasingly inflexible. At the rare parties they were now able to attend, his conversation was confined to shop and a discussion of the latest TV soap saga. Watching television was, in fact, both his and Mary's major spare-time activity.

He was often moody, irritable with his family and experienced bouts of gloom when his whole life seemed pointless.

Mary too had put on a little weight, but she still went swimming regularly and had managed to give up smoking when carrying her first child. Her social life was limited to occasional coffee mornings with neighbours and the exchange of gossip. Their earlier friends had dispersed and neither had found the time or energy to replace them. Most were now selected for convenience, from colleagues at work or close neighbours, rather than as a result of mutual attraction.

Sex had become more of a habit than a pleasure, and John found it increasingly difficult to perform, a failure he gloomily accepted – together with his lack of energy, falling hair and sagging stomach – as another inevitable consequence of growing older.

As they advanced through middle adulthood, the deficiencies in their lives could be summarised as follows:

MENTAL	*PHYSICAL*
	Overweight
Worries (work,	Smoking
family's future,	Drinking in excess
family's health)	Psycho-physiological diseases
Chronic stress	resulting from stress
Lack of interest	Insufficient exercise
Frustration at not	Impoverished sex life
achieving potential	

Their lifestyle deficiencies were reflected in their attitudes and appearance. John looked far older than his chronological age. Cautious and conservative, his energy, enthusiasm and self-confidence were at a low ebb. Mary, because she had always been more concerned about her looks and taken better care of herself, showed less obvious signs of the passing years. But her invisible aging was no less severe. She complained of feeling frequently depressed, unhappy and frustrated. She believed her intellect had gone into an irreversible decline and was afraid to attempt a return to teaching.

John's FAR assessments scores were as follows:

CHRONOLOGICAL AGE: **44**
BIOLOGICAL AGE: **56** (aging factor +12)
PSYCHOLOGICAL AGE: **52** (aging factor +8)
INTELLECTUAL AGE: **51** (aging factor +7)
SOCIAL AGE: **56** (aging factor +12)
OVERALL R:D AGE: **56**

Mary's scores were:

CHRONOLOGICAL AGE: **43**
BIOLOGICAL AGE: **53** (aging factor +10)
PSYCHOLOGICAL AGE: **55** (aging factor +12)
INTELLECTUAL AGE: **55** (aging factor +12)
SOCIAL AGE: **53** (aging factor +10)
OVERALL R:D AGE: **55**

As their results indicate, although Mary was aging less rapidly biologically than John, her rate of psychological and intellectual aging was greater.

Their assessment scores guided them to the most appropriate procedures for inclusion in their FAR programme. After twelve months' work they had succeeded in turning their lifestyles around. John now looked, and sounded, like a much younger man. He had greatly reduced the amount of time spent behind his desk and discovered to his great surprise that, far from becoming less productive, he was actually getting more done and achieving far better results than during his days as a workaholic. He was far more energetic, positive and self-confident. Both his drinking and smoking had been drastically reduced, although he had not given up cigarettes entirely. Regular exercise – they went swimming and went on long, brisk, weekend walks together – had improved his stamina and general fitness.

He and Mary started evening classes, she to learn German, he to study navigation for a boat which he intended to buy shortly. They had widened their circle of friends and enjoyed a far fuller and more rewarding social life. Their sex life had also improved considerably.

Mary, who resumed teaching four months after starting the programme, had overcome her mild agoraphobia and, far from being depressed, was bubbling with vitality and enthusiasm.

FAR did not do all this for them, of course. But it did provide the key which allowed them to unlock their own, previously untapped, resources of creativity and zest for life.

You too can achieve this, by developing a lifestyle which promotes continual regeneration through diet, exercise and your attitude towards living. By liberating those natural powers of rebirth and renewal which lie dormant within mind and body it becomes possible to enjoy not only a longer and healthier life, but greater vitality, fitness and vigour than you ever realised you possessed.

Five: Matters of life and death

> 'Why, sir, his hide is so tanned with his trade
> that he will keep out water a great while; and
> your water is a sore decayer of your whoreson
> dead body.'
>
> (William Shakespeare *Hamlet*)

It has taken two thousand years for the belief of Roman physician Marcus Terentius that 'aging itself is a disease' to receive general – if not universal – acceptance by gerontologists. Aging *is* a sickness of the metabolism, a process of gradual deterioration in physiological and biochemical functioning which, like other bodily ills and ailments, responds favourably to the appropriate treatment.

As I explained in Chapter One, with our present state of knowledge aging cannot be avoided nor death defeated. But we do already have sufficient knowledge to slow down, and in some instances prevent, many of its more unpleasant and debilitating consequences.

In this chapter I shall set the scene for the FAR programme by explaining some of the current theories of aging and demonstrating how Facilitated Active Regeneration can place the prospect of a long and, far more importantly, healthy life within the grasp of anybody prepared to make a modest investment of time, trouble and effort in its procedures.

Aging in action

During normal aging, we are healthiest around the age of ten, but slowly decline from then on. Men attain the peak of their sexual potency about the age of eighteen, when daily secretion of the male sex hormone testosterone, by the Leydig cells in the testes, is at its maximum.

Testosterone promotes the production of sperm and the development of sexual organs and secondary sexual characteristics such as pubic hair and enlargement of the external genitalia. Women don't peak sexually for another twelve years. By puberty, however, some important degeneration is taking place in both sexes, especially in the thymus gland whose key role in combating infection will be discussed later in this chapter.

We achieve maximum physical strength in the mid-twenties. But, already, some signs of aging can be seen in the slight loss of height as deterioration of the vertebral discs brings the spinal bones closer.

By their thirties, people aging normally are passing their physical peak, while the functional efficiency of their body begins declining by around 0.8 per cent each year. Heart muscles gradually thicken, hearing becomes less acute, and the skin loses much of its former elasticity with the appearance of smile and frown lines.

At forty our immune system has usually deteriorated, with lymphocytes (a group of white blood cells which constitute a major weapon in the body's defensive armory) exhibiting a marked decrease in their ability to destroy cancer cells. Hair starts greying and the diameter of follicles decreases. During this decade, the majority of men become long-sighted and get shorter, shrinking by almost one-eighth of an inch compared with their height at twenty.

During the fifties one typically finds a sharp increase in the signs and symptoms of the aging disease. Eyes become short-sighted, sometimes cancelling out the previous long-sightedness and actually correcting poor vision. Female glands stop secreting sex hormones as women enter menopause and leave the reproductive stage of life behind.

Because the rate of production of two chemicals, the enzyme trypsin and the protein hormone insulin, declines the risk of diabetes increases. Taste becomes less sharp. Thumbnails grow more slowly. The skin increasingly sags and wrinkles. A slowing of the metabolism means that food is burnt more slowly and body fat accumulates, often concealing an actual loss of weight through the disappearance of muscle tissues. Although men can remain fertile into their seventies, the production and quality of semen decreases from the fifties onwards. As the vocal cords stiffen and vibrate at a higher frequency a man's voice may rise from C to E-flat.

By the time they have reached sixty, the average person has shrunk by three-quarters of an inch from young adult height, a decade later by a full inch. With only 36 per cent of taste buds still active, taste declines. Arm muscles are only half as strong as they were at twenty.

This then is the normal pattern of aging, the process of growing old and approaching death.

Aging and dying

In Chapter One, I briefly mentioned the statistical research published, in 1825, by the English scholar Benjamin Gompertz. This work appeared in the learned *Philosophical Proceedings of the Royal Society of London*. Entitled 'On the Nature of the Function Expressive of the Law of Human Mortality', Gompertz's erudite paper set out the probability of dying, at different ages, in any one year. He showed that, after thirty-five your chances of dying increase by 8.8 per cent every year, while the probability of dying in any one year approximately doubles every eight years.

The effect of his discovery, which I have calculated for current mortality rates in Western Europe, is illustrated opposite. When you know how to interpret them, these rather dull-looking graph lines provide a fascinating picture of aging in action.

Age is shown along the horizontal axis, and the number of deaths per thousand of the population on the vertical axis. The first thing that strikes one is the marked sex differences. At all ages, especially during the mid to late teens, women run a lower risk of dying in any one year than males. It is only after the age of eighty that the two lines start converging.

Next, consider the early years. From birth, when infant deaths lift the curve just above the zero point, there is a significant drop in mortality rates until around the age of

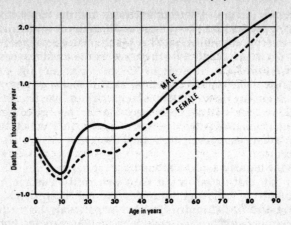

twelve, after which the lines start rising again, indicating an increased risk. The discrepancy between young men and women is due to the greater number of males who die in car accidents. In the USA more than 40,000 men in their teens and early twenties – the average age is twenty-two – are killed in car crashes each year. By the age of thirty-five women are twice as healthy as men, mainly – it it believed – because fewer women smoke. Between thirty-five and seventy-five, their death rate continues to be less than that of males.

How people die
In the West approximately 92 per cent of both sexes die from illness, 5 per cent as the result of various types of accident, while 2 per cent commit suicide and 1.0 per cent are murdered. Heart disease is responsible for the greatest number of fatalities, more than 700,000 US citizens dying this way each year. Number two in the American killing league is cancer (328,000 US casualties per year), followed by strokes (209,000) and diabetes (38,950). Motor cars are the greatest cause of accidental deaths (55,350), then comes drowning (7,380), fire (7,380), electrocution (1,025), hypothermia (334) and flood (205).

During the mid-nineteenth century half the population of the West had died by the age of 40. Today a white male will live to an average of 71.4 years, a white woman to 78.7. Although blacks tend to die earlier than whites, those who make it past the age of 75 have a greater life expectancy. The United States Bureau of Statistics reports that there are now 32,000 centenarians, a 300 per cent increase over twenty years ago. Similar figures can be found throughout the developed world. Half of all the people who have ever lived after the age of 65 are alive today!

In the less developed nations, life expectancy is often less than half that found in the West (where the average for females is 79 years, and for males 73) and Japan (females 80, males 74). Countries whose populations have the lowest average life span include Mali (27 years for both sexes), Chad (males 29, females 35) and Gambia (males 32, females 35).

I have quoted statistics at some length because they provide such a convincing demonstration of the First Law of Le Compte in action. As you may recall from Chapter One, this states that *aging proceeds most rapidly where the deficiencies are greatest and most numerous.*

Aging, deficiencies and death

As major deficiencies in nutrition, hygiene and housing have been eliminated in the developed countries, and major diseases such as tuberculosis, smallpox, chickenpox, cholera and measles either eliminated or brought under control, the quality as well as the quantity of life has increased.

Now science is turning its attention to the other, less obvious and more intractable aspects of the deficiencies which promote degeneration and so lead to aging. To discover what these are, and how researchers are tackling the hazards they pose, we must examine the building blocks of all living organisms, the cells, in some detail.

Why people age

A man in his mid-fifties may feel as youthful as in his

twenties. A woman in her sixties may be almost as active and as alert as she was thirty years earlier. Such vim and vigour are tributes to the power of a positive attitude and, probably, a healthy lifestyle. Yet, no matter how vital and enthusiastic they are in their outlook on life, they will find it hard to conceal from the world the passing of the years.

Their skin will be more wrinkled in appearance, tougher, less elastic to the touch, perhaps mottled with small brown 'age spots'. Even if they have taken plenty of exercise and never smoked, heart and lungs will be less efficient than those of a young adult. Despite all their efforts to hold the ravages of aging at bay, the billions of cells which form the building blocks of their bodies will have deteriorated.

The cells of our body are extremely tiny – about 1,000 could be placed side-by-side on your thumbnail – and highly complex. If we could take a journey inside a cell, our first impression would be of a sphere surrounded by a protective wall known as the membrane. This is a highly selective barrier which allows some substances, such as oxygen and the raw materials from which energy can be produced, free passage while remaining impervious to harmful material.

The cell can be likened to an extremely specialised factory which is designed to manufacture and distribute a single product with great efficiency. The nature of this product depends on the cell's function and is written into the DNA master plan. This is to be found in the nucleus from which the cell's activities are regulated. This contains both DNA, the main blueprint, and RNA, its working instructions. Fuel to run the factory is provided by a chemical called Adenosine Tri-Phosphate (ATP), which is the end-product of digestion. As ATP burns in the presence of oxygen, transported to the cell by the bloodstream, metabolism takes place. It is this essential operation, the production of the energy on which life depends, that, by triggering the cell's deterioration, ultimately comes to produce the symptoms of aging and pose a lethal threat to life itself.

Strange as it may seem, aging human tissue has a lot in common with plastic growing yellow and stiff, paper becoming faded and brittle, and rubber losing its flexibility and finally disintegrating. All suffer a similar fate at the hands of a common enemy – the free radicals. The significance of these potent molecules in human aging was first recognised by the Norwegian chemist Dr Johan Bjorksten. During the Second World War he was employed by an American photographic company on a study of film emulsions. He realised that deteriorations which occurred in the gelatin bases of photographic emulsions resembled those observed in aging cells. In both cases the changes were brought about by the formation of chemical bonds between the long, thin protein molecules which make up the gelatin. The same effect is produced intentionally by tanning animal hides to manufacture leather, and accounts for the difference in appearance and texture between a finished skin and the hide of a living animal. The name Johan Bjorksten gave to these changes in the protein structure was 'cross-linking.'

When Hamlet asks the gravedigger why the corpse of a tanner will last longer in the earth than any other, the man replies with the comment quoted at the start of this chapter. The tanner's body, having absorbed the chemicals with which he spent a lifetime labouring, has developed proteins more resistant to digestion by micro-organisms and less permeable to water.

In our cells, the burning of ATP to produce energy gives rise to potent molecules known as 'free radicals'. Dr Roy Walford, of the UCLA Medical School, one of the world's foremost experts on aging, describes free radicals as 'the great white sharks of the biochemical seas'. More flippantly, gerontologist Alex Comfort compares them to randy males attending conventions, since both are eager to couple with any suitable partner.

By forming links between previously independent protein molecules, free radicals cause them to function with decreasing efficiency. Bjorksten, today the director of the Bjorksten Research Foundation in Madison, Wisconsin, likens cross-linking agents to metal rods with a hook at either end, and asks that we imagine a highly productive factory floor which is suddenly invaded by saboteurs. They use these rods to attach workers to one another, so putting the pair out of action. For a while output and productivity are maintained, since the factory has many more workers than are usually needed and others can become more productive to make up for any shortfall in output.

Inevitably, as time passes, production slows, then declines more sharply until, finally, the factory is completely incapable of operation. The same type of disruption, Bjorksten argues, occurs within the cell as free radicals perform their deadly cross-linking activities. The outer membrane becomes a less effective barrier against invading micro-organisms, so the risk of infection and disease increase. The cell can no longer perform its specialist task so effectively.

Orders from the nucleus are either ignored or inefficiently acted upon. In those cells which regenerate, damage to DNA and RNA means that every duplicate is a less than perfect copy which fails to function correctly. Older cells, being unable to synthesise sufficient protein to perform their roles, are condemned to death.

Free radicals have been implicated in events as serious as cancer and the senile degeneration of Alzheimer's disease. By causing lung tissues to stiffen and become less elastic free radicals contribute to the suffocating disease of emphysema. The once-flexible walls of arteries and veins harden, increasing the risk of a stroke or some other major disorder of the cardiovascular system. In arteriosclerosis, for example, free-radical molecules convert cholesterol from its benign form to a type which clogs arteries. They render enzymes inactive and degrade the fluids which lubricate our joints.

Cross-linking also brings about changes in collagen, a substance which accounts for some 40 per cent of total body protein and provides the supporting structure of the cells, as well as being found in bones, skin, cartilage and connective tissue. It is the hardening of collagen which creates the difference between the smooth, soft skin of a child and the calloused, wrinkled features of an old person. The deterioration of collagen leads to a stiffening of the joints, which limit the competitive careers of world-class gymnasts to the first twenty years of life. Thickening collagen 'chokes off' the flow of nutrients to surrounding tissues, starving them of blood and oxygen. Food is no longer transported to the cells or waste products removed so successfully.

You can estimate the extent of cross-linking in your own skin by placing one hand flat, stretching the fingers and pinching up a fold of skin as high as is comfortably possible. Hold for six seconds and then release. The more rapidly the fold disappears, the smaller the extent of collagen cross-linking which has occurred.

As well as the effects of the body's normal metabolic processes, cross-linking is stimulated by natural and man-made hazards such as cosmic rays, radiation and nuclear fall-out, X-rays and even the luminous dial of a watch. A major cause of cross-linking in the skin is exposure to ultra-violet light, either from sunshine or sunbeds. Even when sitting in the shade, each quart of air around you on a bright, sunny day contains about a billion highly potent free radicals. Ketones, present in larger quantities in the blood of diabetics, are powerful cross-linking agents, as are many metal ions, including copper, cadmium and aluminium. Smog and cigarette smoke contain acetaldehyde, a dangerous cross-linker. Acetaldehyde is also produced by the liver from alcohol which we drink, and manufacture naturally in our body.

Bjorksten's theory has proved an invaluable contribution to understanding the aging process. A fellow researcher, Dr Harry Demopoulos, describes it as 'as important an advance in medicine as Pasteur's germ theory of disease'.

But cross-linking is not the only factor in the aging disease. There is also, for example, the gradual accumulation of unwanted products which result in a clogging and/or poisoning of the whole system. This detritus includes both waste, produced by cells during their normal metabolic functioning, and non-waste molecules that build up when cells manufacture proteins, lipids, cholesterol and other substances more rapidly than they can be removed. This accretion of biological garbage is responsible for creating brown 'age spots', as deposits of a substance called lipofuscin build up beneath the skin.

Since the speed at which waste products accumulate and

cross-linking occurs is determined by the rate at which metabolism takes place, one would expect there to be a link between metabolic rate and lifespan. The faster the pace of life, the shorter that life is destined to be.

This is, indeed, just what one does find when comparing longevity and metabolic rate across a number of species. Small animals live life in the fast lane. They breathe more quickly, pump blood more energetically and burn food more rapidly than larger ones. A shrew lives just over a year, a mouse for between two and three years, while an elephant usually reaches half a century. But if one counts lifespan by heartbeats, all three live for approximately the same amount of time. The heart of a five-ton elephant beats about 30 times per minute or 800 million times in fifty years. A 30- gram mouse, whose heart rate is around 600 beats per minute, takes only two and half years to reach the same total. The shrew's heart, racing at over 1,000 beats per minute, gets there in under twelve months.

The primary reason for these differences is the need for all warm-blooded animals to maintain body temperature within critical limits. If our own internal temperature rises, or falls, by more than about 6 degrees for any length of time we go into a coma and die. A good 80 per cent of the calories from the food we eat is burned up in maintaining the body's core temperature at 98.4 degrees fahrenheit.

The rate at which heat is lost depends not only on outside temperature but also on the relationship between an animal's surface area and its body mass. This means that small creatures lose heat far more rapidly than large ones. Compare the bulk and surface area of a mouse with those of an elephant, for instance, and the problems faced by small mammals become obvious. If they are not to suffer hypothermia even on the mildest days, they must generate the heat needed by burning food extremely rapidly. Mice have a resting metabolic rate twenty times that of the elephant and thirty times that of man.

Although both mice and men expend around 700 calories per gram of tissue throughout their lives, the mouse with approximately thirty times more surface area per gram of body mass than ourselves must burn its calories thirty times faster. Interestingly, it lives approximately one thirtieth as long.

Bjorksten's theory suggests that deterioration could be dramatically reduced if the free radicals responsible for cross-linking were eliminated before they could do their deadly work. Such chemicals do exist and are often referred to as 'anti-oxidants', a wildly misleading term, since preventing oxidation by the cells would be fatal. A more accurate term is anti-cross-linking agent (ACLA). These agents function in one of three ways. They prevent damaging free radicals from forming in the first place, or either remove or destroy them once they have formed but before too much damage has been done. In each instance the integrity of the cell would be preserved and it could go on functioning, and replicating, without suffering the seriously adverse consequences of regeneration. The body has evolved its own defences against cross-linking, like the enzyme superoxide dismutase. The more long-lived an animal, the more superoxide dismutase it possesses.

But can nature be given a helping hand? Research suggests that this is indeed possible.

Among several promising ACLAs investigated is a chemical called butylated hydroxytoluene (BHT) which is widely used as a food preservative. In a series of experiments conducted by Professor Denham Harman of the University of Nebraska, mice fed on a diet which included BHT have lived significantly longer than animals given the same nourishment minus the anti-cross-linking agent. Professor Harman was able to demonstrate that mice with even a small amount of BHT added to their food lived nearly twice as long as the control animals. Although his work offers tantalising prospects for considerably inhibiting the aging process and prolonging human life, the research remains at the laboratory stage.

There are, however, a number of readily available and entirely safe substances whose potency as ACLAs has been well demonstrated. These include vitamins A, B1, B5, B6, C, & E, together with the minerals zinc and selenium. This last substance may also act as a detoxifier for several extremely harmful metals often present in the modern urban environment, such as mercury and lead. By giving rats a combination of vitamins C and B1, together with cysteine, an amino-acid found in eggs, an American researcher called Dr Herbert Sprince and his co-workers were able to protect rats injected with doses of acetaldehyde sufficient to kill 90 per cent of unprotected animals. While none of the ACLAs currently available are capable of entirely preventing cross-linking, they are able to safeguard the cells from much damage by free radicals.

Vitamins and minerals have a key role in Facilitated Active Regeneration. You'll find details in Chapter Eight.

Cross-linking and the accumulation of waste products are not the only reason why degeneration occurs. Another likely cause lies in the declining effectiveness of a key element in the body's immune system, an organ called the thymus.

The role of the thymus

Tucked away behind your breastbone, located just above the heart, is a two-lobed, ductless organ called the thymus. During the second century BC, the Greek physician Galen believed that this was the seat of the soul, and although his theory was soon discredited the precise function of the thymus remained a matter of considerable doubt and speculation until twenty-five years ago. Before then some researchers believed it might have no important role to play at all.

At birth the thymus weighs around 250 grams and is about the size of a walnut. It continues developing until puberty, when all growth ceases and the organ starts to degenerate. Involution continues throughout life, so that by the age of sixty it has shrivelled to a 3-gram clump of cells. Although the thymus continues working throughout its life, output peaks between birth and five years, and declines sharply from the age of forty onwards.

Some of the mystery surrounding the function of the thymus was removed in 1961 after researchers from the University of Minnesota removed the organ from newborn mice and found, to their surprise, that the animals not only failed to grow but died from massive infections. This strongly suggested that the thymus played a crucial role in the body's immune system.

The next question was what hormone it produced, since none had been discovered. An answer was provided by the biochemist Abraham White and the immunologist Allan Goldstein, at the Albert Einstein College of Medicine in New York. Using recently slaughtered calves in a New York abattoir as a source for the organ, they were able to extract a group of thymic hormones which they named thymosins.

Thymosins are responsible for the production and function of a group of white blood cells known as T cells. Central to the body's immune mechanism, T cells come in three types: *killer* cells which attack both cancer cells and invading organisms, *helper* cells which assist in the production of antibodies, and *suppressor* cells which prevent the immune system attacking its own body.

T cells are a very special type of defender, providing not just the brawn of the body's immune system but also its brains. Unlike scavenging phagocytes, which literally eat invading organisms (the word means 'cell-eater') T cells are able precisely to identify foreign substances or invading organisms. To perform this remarkable feat, T cells possess a set of molecules which, like a precision lock, can only be turned on by an exactly fitting key. This key comprises the unique set of molecules carried by a particular invading organism, or antigen. As Steven Mizel and Peter Jaret point out in their book *In Self Defence*, the implications of such a specific response are staggering.

> Scientists estimate that there are more than one million potential antigens, one million different kinds of molecules – from ragweed pollen to the surface antigens of microbes and virally infected cells – that will mark them as foreign, and to which the body will respond by triggering an immune response.

The healthier you are, the stronger and more effective your immune system will be and the greater your ability to resist infections. As the thymus shrivels, the immune system becomes less and less successful in fighting off infections.

Goldstein and his research colleagues have also found that thymosin stimulates the brain to produce a wide range of substances, including beta endorphins (the body's natural opiate) and ACTH, a hormone which regulates cortisone production and helps relieve rheumatoid arthritis.

Some researchers believe that by giving people thymosin the deficiencies caused by the atrophy of this vital organ can be made good. In a landmark study, William Ershler of the University of Vermont School of Medicine used white blood cells taken from university students and volunteers over the age of sixty-five, all of whom had received anti-tetanus jabs, to explore the effect of thymosin on human lymphocytes. Ershler found that thymosin stimulated the white blood cells of his elderly subjects to produce as many tetanus antibodies as those of young people. In later trials he looked at thymosin's ability to assist elderly people produce antibodies against flu. The results are sufficiently promising to indicate that injecting thymosin together with a flu vaccine could significantly improve the protection afforded to people over sixty.

In another project, patients suffering from lung cancer were given thymosin together with radiation therapy. They remained free from the disease for significantly longer than those treated by the same methods of radiation, but without the thymosin. The US National Cancer Institute found these results so promising that they have funded further research. Thymosin supplements have been given to pre-AIDS patients, and a considerable enhancement of the immune system has been reported. Although aging is not caused by any virus, the effects on the immune system are in many ways similar to increasing risks from infections and some kind of malignancies. It may be, therefore, that thymosin could be given as a further aid to longevity.

While thymosin is not, at present, available outside the laboratory the good news is that there are several readily obtainable substances which stimulate the growth of the thymus and its output of hormones. These include vitamins A, C and E, and the minerals selenium and zinc. When vitamin E was added to the feed of chickens, for example, the birds were better able to withstand bacteria and viruses.

They even showed greater resistance to inoculations with living cancer cells.

Vitamin A has been found capable of doubling the size of the thymus, while vitamin C assists by increasing the activity of white blood cells. It also stimulates the cells' production of interferon, a potent anti-viral and anti-cancer substance. Certain foodstuffs, including pineapple and papaya, contain enzymes which enhance the immune system. These are included in the FAR diet procedures described in Chapter Nine.

In this chapter I have focused on those aspects of biological aging which can, experience suggests, be brought under a fair degree of control. In the next I shall describe the practical steps by which the mind can be made to exert a regeneration-enhancing effect over these bodily processes.

Six: Hope and the healthy heart

> 'Hope is itself a species of happiness, and, perhaps,
> the chief happiness which this world affords.'
>
> (Dr Johnson)

Many people grow old from the inside out. Victims of this form of aging have little faith in either themselves or the future. Their attitudes and beliefs betray the fact that life has broken them. They have lost their ambitions and ceased to dream. They have given up hope.

Hope is the energising force which nourishes and sustains us. Describing his experiences in a Nazi concentration camp, psychologist Bruno Bettelheim recalls that once a prisoner had lost the will to live, death followed rapidly. 'Therefore if one gave up hope, one lost the ability to go on with the difficult and painful struggle survival required and so one died in a short time.'

The loss of hope is a major cause of accelerated degeneration. Those without it are usually depressed and anxious. They wake up early and find it hard to go back to sleep. They become lethargic and indifferent to their surroundings, incapable of raising themselves from the despair into which they have sunk. Memory and concentration may be so impared that they are incapable of solving even simple problems or making everyday decisions.

When chronic, hopelessness can adversely affect the body's immune system, as well as increasing the risk of hypertension, heart disease, ulcers and other psychogenic illnesses. Researchers at Yale University have found that people who approach life with pessimism have a larger proportion of suppressor cells in their blood samples then those who maintain a hopeful, optimistic outlook. Since suppressor cells are believed to undermine the system's resistance to tumour growth, this could be the link between attitudes towards living and susceptibility to diseases, including cancer.

Of all the things we must do to ensure a long and healthy life, remaining hopeful in the face of adversity is frequently the most difficult, but always the most essential. In this chapter I shall explain how hope is born, why it so easily dies and what can be done to safeguard this most precious of your life-enhancing possessions.

Life and the death of hope

During the mid-seventies, an American psychologist named Martin Seligman, then a young graduate student at the University of Pennsylvania, made an important observation about dogs who had failed in a learning experiment. Researchers were attempting to train them to avoid an electric shock by jumping a barrier. Most of the animals had no difficulty at all in mastering this simple strategy and, after the first shock, learned to avoid all further punishment. But one group of dogs never even tried to escape. Rather than seek a way of avoiding the painful experience they simply sat helplessly in the cage. When he discovered these dogs had, previously, been given unavoidable shocks Seligman hypothesised that this experience had taught them all escape attempts were futile. They no longer expected to exert any control over what happened to them and had given up even trying. They had lost hope.

Seligman named this response 'learned helplessness'.

There are many people whose experiences cause them to change hope for helplessness. As a result of numerous disappointments, set-backs and failures they come to the view that nothing they attempt will ever succeed. Once this belief has taken root they stop even trying to change their situation for the better. They conclude that it will be easier and far less distressing to sit back rather than fight back.

But, of course, under very similar circumstances some people do pick themselves up and start all over again. When confronted by personal tragedy or professional disaster not everybody gives up hope. Many, despite frequent disappointments, remain confident and optimistic. Love may cause them pain, but they don't reject the hope of ever finding it. Friends may let them down but they never become hopeless about friendship. They may admit to feeling hurt, resentful, frustrated or disillusioned from time to time, but what they'll never admit is defeat.

It is on this choice, between fighting on in hope or falling back in despair, that a healthy longevity depends. Two hundred years ago, the English philosopher Thomas Hobbes commented: 'There is no such thing as perpetual tranquillity of mind, while we live here; because life itself is but motion, and can never be without desire, nor without fear, no more than without sense.'

But while we may be unable to escape life's blows or avoid its anguishes, we can take steps to ensure that hopeful perseverance becomes a more probable outcome than hopeless resignation.

Dreaming and hoping

Hope is always associated with ambition or dream. Once you stop dreaming, having ambitions and striving for goals you also cease to hope.

Research by Roger Gould at the University of California in Los Angeles has shown that there are several age-related stages in life, each of which has its special sets of goals. During our twenties, the emphasis is on settling down and starting a family. We dream of finding a suitable partner, falling in love, developing a warm relationship, making a home and raising children.

During our thirties, the dreams become rather more complicated and less clearly focused. Problems seem to become more intractable, solutions harder to find, more difficult to implement or less satisfactory in their outcomes. We have an increasing sense of unease about what the future may hold. 'After the age of twenty-nine there is a decline in the feeling that "I would be quite content to remain as old as I am now",' reports Gould. 'A harbinger of the feeling in the early thirties that life looks a bit more complex and difficult than it did back in the roaring twenties.'

The forties are often a time of dissatisfaction and a decreasing sense of well-being. Many of our personal and professional dreams of the twenties have been fulfilled, a career established, a home made, children reared and sent out to make their own way in life, promotions gained, material comforts secured, a measure of security achieved.

Yet, despite these attainments, the forties are frequently a time for regrets. People look back and realise how many of their earlier dreams still remain unfulfilled, while those that have been realised may not always have brought with them the anticipated happiness and satisfaction. There appear to be far fewer options available. Life, which once seemed like a broad highroad with endless interesting turnings to be explored along the way has become an increasingly narrow, high-walled street.

During the fifties there is increasing concern with health. Goals tend to be fewer and shorter term. There is a sense of mental and physical decline, the feeling of not being able to accomplish the things which could be done with ease ten years earlier.

By the sixties our goals are usually far more modest, and a quiet life becomes the ambition of many. These changing dreams are mirrored by changes in the number and intensity of hopes.

The changing nature of dreams and goals described above illustrates a second important point about hope. Our greatest hopes and most exciting dreams almost always involve human relationships.

Lost dreams and lost hope

In 1969 T.H. Holmes and R.H. Rahe devised a Schedule of Recent Life Experiences, consisting of forty-three possible events ranked according to their impact on one's life and the degree of readjustment necessary to cope with them. Heading this list, with a maximum crisis score of 100 points, was the death of a partner. Divorce was next with 73 points, followed by marital breakdown with 65. Also rated as highly stressful were being fired or made redundant (47 points), and retirement (45 points). Experiencing a major life event not only led to depression and anxiety but also increased the risk of physical illnesses, including hypertension and heart disease.

The link between life events and hopelessness is clear. In bereavement we lose all hope of a continued loving companionship, in the break-up of a marriage the hope of emotional security and affection. Redundancy, dismissal or retirement threaten hopes of financial security, the status that comes from employment and the opportunity for further advancement.

This means that we are always at the mercy of those who, because of their position, can destroy our hopes. The unfaithful lover, dishonest business partner, ungrateful employer or disloyal friend have the power to shatter, in just a few moments, years of carefully nurtured dreams.

Sometimes hope dies almost instantly. The overheard phone call that reveals your partner is having an affair, the careless comment which shows a friend has betrayed your trust, the summons to the boss's office which means the end of a career. The anguish and sadness of such an abrupt loss of hope can age a person virtually overnight.

I clearly recall one of my clients whose wife was killed by a drunken driver while cycling home from work. On his visit immediately before this tragedy he was a fit, energetic, confident man who ran his own printing business. Athletic and health-conscious, his biological age was ten years less than his fifty-two chronological years. When I saw him again, only a few days after his wife's death, his appearance was that of an unhealthy man in his sixties. He looked grey, moved and spoke slowly. His face was ashen, the features crumpled. Such a physical reaction to great psychological distress is, of course, far from rare, but one anticipates a gradual recovery as grief subsides.

Sadly, in his case, no such return to normality occurred. He continued to age rapidly and died a few years later, having been transformed by sadness into a shuffling, dispirited shadow of his former self.

I contrast his fate with that of a woman in her early sixties whose husband died after a long and painful illness during which she nursed him devotedly. Although stricken by grief for many months, as her whole life had centred on ensuring his happiness, she courageously rebuilt her life. She learned to drive a car, made many new friends, joined clubs and societies, travelled abroad and so started to dream, and hope, again. Two years after her husband died she looked, and behaved, many years younger than her chronological age.

But while we may well feel crushed by an unexpected trauma which destroys our dreams, hope can also be lost far less dramatically, through the slow accumulation of minor disappointments and frustrations. A woman who has devoted her life to raising a family and caring for her husband may find her dreams fading to nothing but a distant memory. Someone who has devoted years of effort and energy to a career may wake up one morning and find that their dreams suddenly seem trivial or petty.

There is no sudden crisis, no unforeseen loss of job, betrayal or abandonment. Just the gradual grinding-down of one dream and the failure to create any others.

Yet while relationships of one kind or another underlie the loss of both kinds of dreams (cardiologist Dr Peter Nixon has coined the term 'people poisoning' to describe these assaults on our hopes), it is a dangerous error to become so cynical about others that you avoid all but the most superficial of human contact. As Tennyson wrote in *In Memoriam*:

> I hold it true, whate'er befall,
> I feel it, when I sorrow most;
> 'Tis better to have loved and lost
> Than never to have loved at all.

The importance of warm relationships – not just with a sexual partner, but also with good friends and loving relatives – cannot be too strongly emphasised. While people have it in their power to destroy the dreams of others, they also serve as a powerful antidote to anxiety, and a major safeguard against the loss of hope.

The power of human warmth to sustain our emotional health at times of crisis was recently demonstrated by two Sussex University researchers, Win Bolton and Keith Oatley, in a study of the effects of long-term unemployment.

They interviewed men who had just lost their jobs, assessed their level of depression and explored the extent of their social contacts, by asking about the number of relatives and friends they had, how often they saw them and how close was their relationship with them. None of these men was, at that time, especially depressed and their social network was neither better nor worse than a similiar group of men still in employment. Eight months later, those still without work were interviewed again. By this time several had become significantly depressed by their inability to find another job. Those who had suffered the highest levels of depression, however, were the ones with the fewest friends and relatives with whom to talk about their troubles.

Oatley and Bolton believe that what is lost when you become unemployed, suffer a bereavement or experience some similar crisis is what they term 'mutuality'.

Mutuality implies a predictable relationship with other members of the community in which one lives. It is on such relationships that our sense of self depends and through them that our dreams are sustained. 'As an employee one experiences oneself as worthy of respect from one's employer,' comments Keith Oatley, 'a productive member of the community paid a respectable wage, able to provide for one's family and so on. Without a job the possibility of experiencing these qualities is removed.'

Such findings strongly suggest that depression is not, typically, a mental disorder. There is nothing disordered or wrong in the minds of people who become depressed. The reason why more women than men become depressed, and why depression is often related to a lower socio-economic class, is that these people have a greater possibility of things going wrong in their lives, and fewer social or economic resources for dealing with things which do go wrong.

However, there is also evidence that personality plays a role in depression. People differ in their ability to put new plans into operation after a setback and in their dependence on external structure in their life. The most important factor, according to Seligman and his co-workers, is how people explain bad happenings to themselves when reality is ambiguous. Such explanations may be global or specific, internal or external, stable or unstable.

Suppose, for instance, that a relationship ends unhappily. If you ascribe its failure to something which is stable across time – 'I always make a mess of my love life' – then you are going to anticipate the same thing happening again and this could lead to a loss of hope and a sense of helplessness. Again, if your explanation is global – 'I can never get anybody to love me' – rather than specific – 'I cannot get that person to love me' – you will feel increasingly incapable of achieving a loving relationship. Finally, an internal explanation – 'I am solely to blame for what's gone wrong, my partner was not at fault' – rather than an external – 'there were faults on both sides' – also increases the risk that you will abandon hoping for a good relationship in the future.

If you always give global, stable, internal explanations for failure, such as 'I am stupid', then it is far less likely that you will dream of intellectual success. If, however, you explain setbacks in specific, unstable and external terms – 'I certainly messed that up, but I know I can do better the next time, especially if I get the right breaks' – you are far more likely to go on hoping and dreaming.

The explanations we offer ourselves in stressful situations play a role in how we cope with that stress and its likely effects on health and longevity. In a study of sixty-nine women who underwent a mastectomy for breast cancer, it was found that their attitude towards the disease significantly influenced their chances of recovery. Five years after the operation, 75 per cent of those who reacted by fighting back, or denied that they had ever been sick, were still alive and showed no recurrence of the cancer. But only 35 per cent of those who helplessly or stoically accepted the disease remained alive or had no recurrence of the cancer.

The greatest risk of hope being lost and a sense of helplessness developing occurs when, after a severe loss, you are left with no clear role to play and, apparently, no means of creating a new one. Your previous role, as mother, father, lover, employee, employer and so on is no longer available, but because you explain the loss in a negative, restricted manner you cannot see any way in which to put something new in its place.

In part it seems that this inability to reconstruct your life after things have gone wrong stems from having enjoyed an overly dependent relationship on one other person, a parent or partner. This prevents one from learning the skills needed for dealing with setbacks in a constructive manner.

Without in any way diminishing the warmth and intimacy of a close relationship the risk of painfully lost hope can, to some extent, be reduced by never allowing oneself to become overly dependent on another person. That is not to say one should avoid becoming involved in a warm and intimate relationship. Indeed, both human experience and a mass of research data testify to the fact that such a relationship is one of the most important elements of a healthy longevity.

But such a relationship need not and must not demand as its price the total dependence of one partner on the other. Ideally, each will relate to the other in a way which is both involved yet independent. Eric Berne, founder of transactional analysis, describes such close yet autonomous partnerships as being between two adults. Highly dependent relationships, by contrast, occur when one adult chooses to act the role of a parent while the other plays the part of a child.

Dreams and dilemmas

Dependency is especially likely to arise when one or both partners make unwarranted assumptions about the nature of their relationship. This can create one of two sorts of emotional dilemma. The first has been described by Dr Anthony Ryle as a dilemma of 'false dichotomy', since available options are seen in terms of 'Either . . . or'. For instance a person might tell themselves: 'Either I must depend entirely on my partner or I shall be abandoned.'

A second form of dilemma occurs in the form of 'If . . .

then.' A man may think to himself: 'If my wife loves me then she will rely on me entirely.'

While such beliefs operate at a subconscious level, they exert considerable influence over behaviour and emotions. For instance, a woman trapped by the first dilemma – 'either depending on or abandoned by' – may become anxious if she seeks a less dependent role. Daughters who give up the chance of personal happiness to care for an aging mother, for example, may be trapped by the dilemma: 'Either a loving, selfless daughter or a heartless ingrate' or assume that: 'If truly loving then endlessly sacrificing.'

Social and cultural pressures make it more likely that women than men will become ensnared by these sorts of dilemmas and find their world shattered as the hope invested in the relationship is dashed, either through death or desertion.

There is no easy way out of such a situation and, unfortunately, even recognising that you have been trapped by such a dilemma is seldom going to remove it. The stronger the emotions associated with an assumption the harder it is to bring about any changes. A person who makes the unconscious association 'If I am to be loved then I must never assert myself' is bound to find early attempts at becoming more independent extremely painful.

Futhermore, should they persist in this course of action the other person involved is quite likely to exert emotional pressure to restore the, for them, advantageous outlook. The dependent mother, for example, will have developed her own dilemmas within that relationship, perhaps assuming: 'Either looked after by or abandoned entirely' or 'If not dependent on then not loved by.'

These feelings will work against any attempt she might make to become less reliant on her child. As the child struggles to achieve greater independence both their sets of assumptions will be challenged. They may become angry at the other person for seeking to challenge their role and rebuke them with a bitter 'How can you treat me like this after all I have done for you?'

In a marriage, the desire by one partner to enjoy greater

freedom may lead to accusations that she, or he, is being irresponsible, unreasonable or unloving.

If, on reflection, you feel you may have become the victim of such a trap and that this is making you overly dependent on one person, it will be well worth while exploring ways in which you might achieve greater independence. But do not assume that the transition from dependency to autonomy can be an easy one, or that you will not face opposition from the person on whom you have come to rely.

While there cannot be any cook-book recipe for sustaining a hopeful outlook on life, here are seven practical steps that provide useful safeguards.

One – Be a dreamer
When we are young the world seems filled with possibilities. As the years pass it appears increasingly full of impossibilities. We become so weary of inevitable setbacks, or so frustrated by failures, that it seems easier to stop dreaming and give up striving.

It is essential to remain a dreamer, seek out new challenges, set yourself goals and cherish the pleasures which each new age can provide. Don't be resentful about lost chances or regretful over past mistakes but look forward with anticipation for the chances, opportunities and rewards – whatever you conceive them to be – that tomorrow may yield. Set yourself goals, some easy to achieve, others involving a greater effort for a richer reward.

Have several dreams in every area of your life: work, social, family. That way when some fail, as they inevitably must, you'll be sustained by the remainder. Never use your age – at any age – as an excuse for not attempting something new. By varying the lengths of time needed to bring each to fruition you ensure a continual flow of stimulating and hope-engendering activity.

Consider all the areas of your life where you have dreams and decide which ones you should make come true first. Don't leap at the first one which comes to mind but consider several. Often there will be links between different dreams so that fulfilling one makes it easier to achieve others.

Build on your strengths and bring greater excitement into your life. Where possible do what *you want to do* instead of just what others expect you to do. Let your own wishes, not a sense of duty, dictate their choice.

Do not assume that the only worthwhile dreams are those associated with advancing your career or making yourself more financially secure. While it is perfectly natural to be ambitious, purely materialistic dreams usually lead to disappointment when they are the only ones accomplished. To experience the greatest fulfilment in life, spread your dreams over all areas of life.

Dreams which bring something new into your life are usually more fun to work on, than those which take something out of it. If your dream is about losing weight, for instance, it is better to adopt the positive approach of taking more exercise than the more negative one of depriving yourself of favourite foods.

Two – Be a doer

Never wait until you know exactly what you ought to be doing. Learning how to do something correctly after messing it up three times in a row is better than never trying at all. Suppose, for instance, that you feel lonely and long for an intimate relationship. Then you fall for somebody at a party and dream about meeting him, or her, again. How can you do it? Your mind fills with plans. Why not throw a party and invite the person, or ask a mutual friend to let him, or her, know your feelings. Perhaps you should phone and suggest going to the cinema. But you just can't make up your mind about the best approach. While you are dithering that person gets involved with somebody else. So always be a doer, not just a dreamer.

When planning your best course of action be imaginative. Consider what practical skills, knowledge, experience and other resources you can bring to bear on the task. Think about friends, neighbours, relatives or colleagues who might be able to help in making your dreams come true.

Three – Reward yourself along the way

Always feel good about your achievements but never be too downcast by setbacks since these are bound to occur and, what's more, are likely to be more frequent events than successes. Playwright George Bernard Shaw remarked that, 'When I was a young man I observed that nine out of ten things I did were failures. I didn't want to be a failure so I did ten times more.'

Learn from your failures, then forget them. If there is somebody you can trust to offer support then don't be afraid to ask them to reward you by praise when things go well, and encouragement when they go wrong. But choose your friends carefully. He, or she, must accept you as you and not have any burning desire to change you.

Sustaining hope means going out and doing things, rather than worrying about them or endlessly pondering why a particular state of affairs has arisen. Such insight is often interesting but, on its own, no amount of self-knowledge will bring about lifestyle changes. You never achieve anything with good intentions alone. It involves trial, error, perseverance and that first, essential step into the unknown.

Four – Check that your hopes are realistic

As I have explained, unreasonably high hopes may be attached to perfectly attainable goals. When this happens you feel a sense of let-down and disappointment even though you have achieved everything targeted for. Reality-test your hopes. Pitch them too high and you are probably headed for a painful – perhaps fatal – fall.

In an article entitled *The Good Die Younger* (Science, December 1985) writer Ronnie Wacker provided the perfect illustration of how unrealistic hopes can lead to accelerated aging.

Everbody in the small, friendly, old-people's home loved

Mary Frances, a bright, cheerful, undemanding and co-operative lady in her seventies. She was in good health, had a large circle of friends outside the home, and was well liked by other residents. Then the home closed and she was transferred to a large, impersonal institution. Soon afterwards she sank into a depression, then into apathy. She took to her bed. Six months later she was dead.

Wacker contrasts Mary's fate with that of eighty-one-year old Harry, who was 'ill, suspicious and hostile'. In an atmosphere which struck friendly Mary down, irascible Harry thrived. The key to their different fates can be found in their different expectations of life.

'If hopes are too great,' says Sheldon Tobin of the University of Chicago, 'they can be too easily thwarted.' When the expectations are unreasonable they cannot long survive a confrontation with reality and will be crushed by defeat. 'Harry,' Wacker explains, 'was neither too hopeful nor hopeless. . . . Mary Frances, however, accustomed to looking on the bright side, was overcome by the reality of her surroundings.'

This doesn't mean one shouldn't look on the bright side, be optimistic, have dreams or fantasise about wishes coming true. But it is one thing to build castles in the air, quite another to try and live in them.

Be objective not just over your chances of success but about the amount of happiness, contentment and pleasure even a successful accomplishment will provide. Try not to expend too much time and effort in tasks which have no merit or interest in themselves but are merely the means to an end.

You may well find that, on reaching the end, your investment was simply not worth while. The more goals you are working towards at any one time, the less likely it is that any one of them generated unrealistically high hopes.

Five – Banish irrational beliefs
Avoid global, stable and internal explanations for failures and try to see them, instead, as specific, unstable and external events. This will be far easier to do if you make

certain your hopes are not founded on irrational beliefs, about oneself or others.

A belief in the need to be totally loved
Many people firmly hold to the view that it is essential to be loved and admired by everybody: family, friends, even strangers. They set as their goal in life to be universally loved and approved of.

They feel that unless they are totally loved, they must be bad, unworthy, inadequate people who deserve to be rejected. In pursuit of this belief they are constantly pleasant, co-operative and agreeable. They never assert themselves and hardly ever protest when others do them down, since this would force them to confront the fact that not everybody does like or deal fairly with them. They always have excuses for other people's hurtful behaviour, usually attributing it to their own inadequacies: 'I'm sure he/she didn't really mean it, I must have been to blame for what went wrong. . . .'

They have an either/or approach to both themselves and their relations. Either a good person whom everybody loves or a bad one nobody could even like. If obliged to confront the fact that some people really do dislike, or even hate, them they can suffer a catastrophic loss of hope.

Should you hold this view, try to see that you will never win the respect and liking of all those you meet and that to be disapproved of, criticised, even very much disliked is not necessarily any reflection on your worth as a human being. Accept, too, that often the antipathy you meet is more a reflection of somebody else's problems than any inadequacy on your part. Never let a fear of arousing wrath prevent you from standing up for your rights or asserting yourself.

If people get upset, that's unfortunate, and I am not suggesting you go out of your way to annoy or distress those close to you. But often upsetting others is an unavoidable part of life. Also accept that being disliked or disapproved of by certain people doesn't make you an unlikable person. Nor does the fact that someone close to you is critical mean that he, or she, no longer likes or loves you.

The quest for perfection

A second widely held irrational belief concerns the importance of always achieving perfection in everything you do. When, as it must, excellence eludes you, this leads to a loss of hope. Closely allied to this belief is the idea that when things turn out badly or people aren't as you wish them to be one's life will be shattered. Here again you are setting yourself up for needless disappointment and disillusionment.

You are probably being too perfectionist each time any of the following creep into your behaviour:

Procrastination. You put off making a start until you can be certain of not making a mistake. Since this can never happen you never begin.

Negative filtering. You focus on criticisms and brickbats rather than the positive points made about one of your favourite projects or pet schemes.

Take account of negative comments, and if they contain any worthwhile ideas incorporate them into the strategy. But never use another person's views as a reason for not doing what you feel you should be doing.

Finished – product thinking. You never get any satisfaction from doing things, only from having done them. This means that everything depends on the finished product. If that turns out fine you feel pleased and filled with hope. But if you slip up at the last minute, all the good and positive things which went into the production get disregarded in your bitter disappointment over a failure to achieve a perfect end result.

Many people, especially younger ones, are convinced that somewhere in the world is the one partner with whom they can have the perfect relationship. Sadly, experience teaches that not only is such perfection unattainable, it is almost certainly very undesirable. This doesn't mean you cannot have and should not seek a warm, secure and loving relationship. Indeed, such a partnership is essential to emotional and physical health. But to idealise either a relationship or your partner is to set up dangerously high and extremely fragile hopes. It is unreasonable and unfair to both of you.

Perfectionism can also damage your enjoyment of, and performance in, sexual activity.

If you had a high positive score on Statement [14] of Assessment Two it could be that part of the problem is that you are striving to reach an unattainable goal.

Perfectionist males often feel that unless they rate as the world's greatest lover, they don't rate at all. Perfectionist women can feel that unless their body is flawless they don't deserve to enjoy sexual fulfilment.

I am what I own
The notion that your worth as a person depends on how much you achieve or produce is an irrational belief which leads people to set themselves highly materialistic goals on the false assumption that the more possessions you have the happier and more hopeful you will be.

Check your beliefs to see how many of them are, if not irrational, then perhaps somewhat unrealistic or unreasonable. By weeding these out you will safeguard yourself against the inevitable disappointment of exaggerated hopes.

Six – Understanding your moods
There are times when the most optimistic and hopeful person feels depressed and disillusioned for no apparent reason. Even emotionally balanced people suffer mood swings which can be quite severe.

Many such variations in mood are caused by our body clocks, those parts of the brain which create daily, or circadian, rhythms. These rhythms involve the regular rise and fall of such things as temperature, alertness, energy levels and hormonal secretion. These are highest towards the evening and lowest in the hour just before dawn. At this time our resistance is weakened and we are most likely to feel depressed and fearful. Napoleon once remarked that he had yet to meet an officer with 'three o'clock in the morning courage'.

The most sensible way to handle the sense of hopelessness which so often occurs around this time is to firmly remind oneself that it is due to a time-related, biochemical response and reflects neither one's true feelings nor actual prospects.

The dark days of winter months also see a fall in hope among many, due to a recently discovered phenomenon called Seasonal Affective Disorder (SAD). The symptoms of SAD include sluggishness, disturbed sleep and a desire to binge on carbohydrates, in addition to feelings of despair and depression.

There is evidence that these black moods relate to the production of a substance called melatonin by the pineal gland, located at the base of the brain. Light falling on the eyes inhibits melatonin production, while in the darkness this is increased. When psychologist Harris Lieberman and his colleague administered melatonin to volunteers at the Massachusetts Institute of Technology their alertness and reaction times were significantly impaired. Dr Norman Rosenthal at the US National Institute of Mental Health finds that he can successfully treat SAD sufferers with light from lamps designed to mimic the sun's spectrum. After exposure to the light for several hours each day, their depression lifts.

Recently melatonin, taken in capsule form, has proved effective in treating jet-lag, but quite how it helps long-haul travellers is not clear. One view is that the substance simply acts as a mild hypnotic and improves normal sleep. But others believe that it may actually reset a body clock disturbed by having travelled through time zones. During dark winter months your own moods will lighten and you will become more hopeful if you get out into the sunshine at every opportunity. Normal artificial light, no matter how bright, cannot help since the spectrum differs from that of natural sunlight.

You may also find that hope is hardest to come by during the spring. April, according to the poet T. S. Eliot is 'the cruellest month', and the statistics offer grim evidence in support of this poetic assumption. There are more suicides and admissions to mental hospitals in this month than any other. The likely cause, according to researchers at the

Clarke Institute of Psychiatry in Toronto, are our inbuilt biological clocks.

These are most likely to be thrown off balance during March and April, as days start getting longer, and again in September and October as they shorten again. If you find yourself prone to weekly, monthly or seasonal mood swings it will be helpful to keep a record of these highs and lows. By monitoring the ups and downs of your emotions, you'll be less likely to get thrown into despair when life seems especially hard to cope with and hope becomes a stranger. Exercise, sound nutrition and keeping yourself stimulated with plenty of worthwhile goals can all help provide a psychological boost at times when your biology is getting you down.

Seven – The breath of hope

When our major life goals are threatened we may behave in one of two ways. The first is attack; we redouble our efforts to achieve the target and attempt to bully or bulldoze any obstacles out of our way. If this tactic fails, as it frequently does, our sense of hopelessness may be twice as intense. We gave it our very best effort and still failed. This severely dents self-esteem, undermines confidence and makes it a little less likely that we'll stick our necks out on anything so challenging for quite a while.

The alternative, but equally unhelpful, strategy is to retreat at the first sign of opposition, throw up our hands in surrender, admit it was all a dreadful mistake and write off our investment in time and energy. Again, such an approach demands a steep price be paid in lost hope. We may feel ourselves worthless, inadequate and incompetent. Avoidance, like attack, reduces the likelihood of our attempting challenging tasks for at least a while.

Both these approaches reduce anxiety: avoidance by withdrawing us from the threatening situation and anger by raising the blood pressure and so increasing the production of certain chemicals which have a sedating effect on the brain. Neither, as we have seen, is a satisfactory answer.

Next time things start going wrong, try to breathe life back into your project and hope back into your outlook by adopting the following procedure.

Remove your shoes, loosen tight clothing and lie down flat on a bed, couch or the floor. Put a small pillow under your neck. Rest the left hand on your stomach and the right against the same side of your chest. Take a deep, slow, breath. Imagine the air is being directed to a spot just below your navel. Feel your stomach swelling as air floods into the lower portions of the lungs.

Now direct the air into the upper parts of the lungs so that your chest expands, pushing the rib-cage outward. Check this is happening with your right hand. Continue to draw in air for a slow count to seven.

Hold the inhalation for a further seven seconds or longer if you can do so comfortably. The more you use this exercise the longer you will be able to hold this breath in your lungs without discomfort and the more oxygen will be absorbed.

Breathe out in the reverse order to the inhalation. Slowly draw in your lower abdomen, pushing the air upwards. Then contract the rib-cage, driving breath from the upper areas of the lungs. This should also take about seven seconds.

Pause, and repeat a further six times, making a total of seven inhalations and exhalations. Now that your body is relaxed and your brain enriched with oxygen, review the steps taken so far in your project. See if you have overlooked anything vital, made an unwarranted assumption which is likely to upset your calculations, placed too much trust in some other person or people.

Consider various alternative options. Explore different approaches and their probable outcomes. If you feel your anger, or anxiety, rising then repeat the breathing exercise and focus on each inhaled and exhaled breath. This centres the mind and prevents you from being overwhelmed by thoughts which are as unhelpful as they are agitating.

Use the same procedure when you are planning some challenging task, coming to terms with a failure, trying to cope with a disappointment, or pick yourself up after being let down by a friend. You'll find that taking time out to relax your body and refresh the brain will breath fresh hope into your outlook.

By following these seven guidelines you should find it easier to avoid many of the worst pitfalls created by high but unrealistic expectations.

Remember that the old saying 'while there's life there's hope' got its message back to front. The truth is that only while there is hope can there be a fulfilling life.

SEVEN: Your long-life brain

'To get a good idea you must get lots of ideas.'

(Linus Pauling)

Your brain was built to last a lifetime. Treated properly it will do just that. Far from suffering an irreversible decline from middle-age onwards, research has shown that not only is it capable of high-level performance at any age but, in some ways, works even better as it grows older. Research has also indicated that:

Memory can function perfectly throughout life
There is no time limit to our ability to master new knowledge and acquire fresh skills
Creativity, problem-solving and decision-making can all improve with age

Old dogs – new tricks

In 1969 some of these important claims were put to the test by Drs Geoffrey Naylor and Elsie Harwood at the University of Queensland. They sought volunteers, among people aged over sixty, for a course in German. Those agreeing to participate had no previous knowledge of the language. They attended a two-hour lesson once a week and studied privately for one hour each day. The ages of those taking part ranged from sixty-three to ninety-one, with an average around seventy years.

In most cases these people had a meagre educational background; more than half had attended only primary school, while others had not even completed this minimal amount of formal education. The lessons were specially designed to remove all competition between students. The only people they were expected to compete with were themselves. The results suprised even the optimistic expectations of the researchers. Only one student dropped out and, just three months later, 81 per cent were sufficiently advanced to take a formal exam normally set for secondary school pupils after three years of studying. More than 70 per cent passed with flying colours. Three months later, they sat a second exam, this time at a standard which chidren would be expected to achieve only towards the end of their school careers. According to Naylor and Harwood,

> The most conservative general statement would be that over 50 per cent of the 'starters' had in six months reached or exceeded the standard expected of fourth-year secondary school children. We believe these results amply demonstrate that a large proportion of the elderly have the capacity to begin and sustain a completely new study in such a way as to add substantially to their intellectual repertoire.

Memory is NOT impaired with age

These findings came as no surprise to Dr Belle Boone Beard, a gerontologist who has devoted half a lifetime to examining the effects of aging on intellectual ability and reckons to have "corresponded with, interviewed, recorded, and photographed more 100-year-olds than any other person on earth, past or present".

Dr Beard is convinced that memory has no upper age limit. What does alter, however, are the things which people feel it necessary to commit to memory as they grow older. While the young absorb information without much discrimination, remembering both the trivial and significant, the relevant and irrelevant, older people memorise only those facts of relevance to them and devote far less time and storage space to unnecessary knowledge.

She has not, however, found any evidence to support the popular belief that people remember the past more clearly than the present as they grow older.

IQ need NOT decline with age

The widely held assumption that intelligence, as measured by standard IQ tests, declines abruptly after a certain age was investigated by psychologist Jon Kangas in a thirty-eight-year follow-up study of forty-eight men and women whose IQ's were first assessed in 1931 while they attended nursery school. The same group were retested in 1941, while at junior school, and again fifteen years later.

The final tests were performed in 1969, thirty-seven years after the first had been administered. Far from noting a deterioration between early childhood and middle age, Kangas found an increase of 20 points between the first and final IQ scores. In nursery school the group mean was 110.7 and this had risen to 130.1 by the final assessment.

Kangas's verdict on his findings reinforces the notion that any aging effects on intellectual performance are most often due to a self-fulfilling prophecy. 'People tend to have a self- image and become what they envisage themselves to be. If you assume you are going downhill you will.'

Brains can work even better with age

The mental procedures used to solve problems and make decisions not only appear to change with age, but actually to become more efficient. A study conducted by Dr James E. Birren and his colleagues at the University of Chicago showed that older people often develop the more effective thinking strategy of considering larger chunks of information at a time. Rather than breaking the task into small components and then working on these, more mature thinkers identified relationships between seemingly unconnected elements more rapidly and discarded irrelevant information more swiftly.

Dr Birren concludes that, provided we take good care of ourselves, it is reasonable to expect the brain to work even better as we get older.

The problem of lost brain cells

Right now you may be wondering how such performance

can be maintained in view of the well-known loss of brain cells throughout life. Surely this physical deterioration, due to the constant death of posmitotic (i.e. non-replaceable) tissue must have a drastic effect on function? It is true that brain cells die in large number every day of our life from around the age of twenty onwards. Some 50,000 perish daily, mainly in the cortex – that area of the brain responsible for intellectual activity. This causes the brain to shrink during the course of normal aging by 10–15 per cent.

Fortunately we have such a superabundance of cells, estimated at 13 billion, plus a further 70 billion supporting cells, that even this seemingly high rate of attrition is of no practical significance provided we protect those remaining with a healthy lifestyle and the right kind of nutrition.

Furthermore, some parts of the brain continue to grow throughout life, the dendrites (thread-like extensions of the neurons which make contact with other cells) being continuously replaced.

How FAR helps

The FAR programme enhances the ability to use one's brain to maximum effect throughout life by improving mental performance in two main ways. Firstly by removing the major barriers to effective thinking which can arise at any age and whose consequences are to limit the range and scope of intellectual functioning. Secondly, by protecting and enriching the brain itself through diet, exercise and supplements.

Here are seven steps to successful thinking:

One – Banish negative beliefs

How many of these statements do you agree with?

1 Curiosity killed the cat
2 I waste too much time day-dreaming
3 Nobody is interested in my opinions
4 You are finished after forty
5 TV is a waste of time

6 There is no substitute for working hard
7 You can't teach old dogs new tricks

If you answered yes to any of them, negative beliefs are undermining your powers of thought. To understand why, let's consider in more detail what those beliefs imply.

1 Curiosity killed the cat.

It's far more dangerous to lack curiosity. The need to discover and learn, to invent and innovate are essential to successful thinking, as we shall see in a moment.

2 I waste too much time day-dreaming.

Never feel guilty about letting your mind wander. That's the way insights are arrived at and new ideas conceived.

3 Nobody is interested in my opinions.

If that's what you believe, then it's probably true. Such self-defeating, negative comments indicate a brain churning in low gear and obsessed by crippling self-pity. If you've got anything worth saying, then people will want to listen.

4 You are finished after forty.

Another unwarranted assumption that quickly turns into a deadly self-fulfilling prophecy. A study of the achievements of 738 highly successful thinkers, both male and female, in all fields of intellectual endeavour, showed that the greatest contributions in both arts and sciences was made by those in their fifties, with output in history and philosophy peaking in the sixties.

Consider also that: Goethe finished the last part of *Faust* just prior to his death aged eighty-three; Freud wrote *Moses and Monotheism* at the age of eighty-three; Michelangelo was working in his studio almost to the day of his death at the age of eighty-nine; Pablo Casals continued playing, conducting and teaching up to the moment he died at ninety-six; Verdi composed *Otello* at the age of seventy-three, *Falstaff* at eighty and *Te Deum* at eighty-five.

5 TV is a waste of time.

Not so. You need to relax your brain from time to time and some mindless TV show can help you do just that. The eminent American psychologist B.F. Skinner says that relaxing with soap operas has helped his brain work better. Even the best mind can't work flat out all the time.

6 There is no substitute for working hard.

Try preparation and inspiration. Workaholic clients of mine who decided to slow down after starting work with the FAR procedures were astonished to find that they not only did more in less time once they slowed the pace, but that the quality of their output was more consistently high. Very often frenetic activity can serve as a substitute for thought and planning. The brain is wasting effort and energy in trying to do something inefficiently which might be completed in half the time with prior thought.

7 You can't teach old dogs new tricks.

This notion is, as we have seen, as absurd as all the others. But it is sufficiently powerful to cause once intellectually able people to give up trying to use their brains effectively beyond a certain age. They are so certain they'll fail on any major mental challenge that they abandon the idea of even attempting to master fresh skills or acquire new knowledge. Morton Puner in his book *To The Good Long Life* comments:

> We are hounded by the notion that memory, intelligence and the ability to learn and be productive must deteriorate, that our mental energies must fail, somewhat slower than our physical energies but in the same way. The idea that mind and memory decline with time is so strongly held that it sometimes becomes self-fulfilling; mind and memory may fail in old age simply because they are expected to.

Two – Cultivate your curiosity

One of the most obvious differences between a brain which is actively regenerating itself and one deteriorating rapidly under the effects of accelerated degeneration lies in the amount of curiosity present.

Curiosity is often curbed early on in life when parents and teachers conspire to make us afraid of asking too many questions. Yet all human discoveries and advances, from the trivial to the tremendous, have only been possible because men and women cultivated their curiosity. We can all benefit by becoming more curious about the world around us. Try these practical ways of enhancing your curiosity:

Be observant

Anybody who has ever tugged burrs from their dog's coat after a walk in the country, or glimpsed a piece of broken glass flashing in their car's headlights at night, has spotted the basis of two of the world's simplest but most profitable inventions. Thistle burrs inspired Swiss inventor Georges de Mestral to create Velcro fabric fasteners, while an Englishman named Percy Shaw came up with the idea of cats'-eye road markings after spotting the gleam of broken glass when driving up his drive one night.

Their genius lay in looking at the familiar and seeing something highly original. Even if you have no interest in inventing or discovering anything, using your brain in that way keeps it lively and alert. Constantly question, ponder and wonder. Never take things for granted.

Seek imperfections

As a young and poorly paid railway engineer Walter Chrysler saved enough from his meagre salary to purchase a $5,000 motor car – not to drive and impress his friends, but to tear apart, carefully and thoughtfully, in search of imperfections in the components and overall design. By identifying and correcting the mistakes of other designers and engineers he was able to found an automobile empire.

Make a 'bug' list of the things which annoy you in your daily life. If you get irritated by them the chances are that millions of other people feel the same way, and by discovering a way of eliminating some of those irritants you may be on your way to a fortune. You'll certainly be keeping your brain in trim.

Don't jump to conclusions

The older we get the richer our mental storehouse of facts and figures. If you collected one new impression each waking second, a modest chore, after forty-five years you would have more than 90 million to play around with. Often it is the very weight of accumulated knowledge which suffocates curiosity. We come to believe we've seen it all, experienced it all, know it all.

In a parable about our limited vision when dealing with the unknown, John Godfrey Saxe describes how six blind men examined an elephant in order to satisfy themselves about the nature of the beast. One felt only its leg and concluded it was like a tree. Another examined the trunk and said it had much in common with a snake. The third explored its tail and convinced himself that an elephant most resembled a rope. The fourth after touching the tusks insisted the beast was like a spear. The fifth man, running his hands over the immense flank, stated firmly that what an elephant really resembled was a wall, while the sixth touched the ear and decided the creature was most like a fan. And so, concludes the writer, these worthy men: 'Disputed loud and long, Each in his own opinion, exceeding stiff and strong. Though each was partly in the right, They all were in the wrong!'

His tale emphasises the danger of what psychologists call premature closure, the risks we run when coming to too firm a conclusion too swiftly. In order to make sense of the world at all we have to filter out all but a tiny minority of the incoming information, and to consider a mere fragment of the stored knowledge available to us.

'To make biological survival possible,' wrote Aldous Huxley in *The Doors of Perception*, 'mind at large has to be funneled through the reducing valve of the brain and nervous system. What comes out the other end is a measly trickle of the kind of consciousness which will help us to stay alive on the surface of this particular planet.'

We must be aware of these limitations and strive to overcome them by never jumping to easy conclusions.

Here is a simple test you might like to try. Just write down the number of squares in the illustration below.

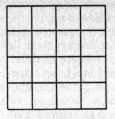

How many did you find? If, like the majority of people, you only noted down sixteen, you made an assumption about what constitutes a square. You probably glanced at the illustration, noted the 4 × 4 arrangement and simply multiplied to come up with your answer. But look again. How about a 2 × 2 square arrangement, or one 3 × 3? And how about the one large square? In fact, the correct answer is thirty.

Build your curiosity by constantly testing out assumptions, beliefs and opinions that are normally taken for granted and accepted without question.

Three – Spot your blind spots
The figure below will help you find your visual blind spot.

15 14 13 12 11 10 9 8 7 6 5 4 3 2 1 ●

Close your left eye. Hold the page at a normal reading distance and focus on the large dot with your right eye. Slowly shift your gaze to the numbers, looking at each one in turn. As you do so remain aware of the black dot which stays in your field of view. At some point along the line, the dot disappears. This is the angle at which the dot falls on that area of your retina where the optic nerve leaves the eye, producing a patch free of light-sensitive cells. Move your gaze back along the line and the black dot reappears.

Locating the visual blind spot is easy, dicovering intellectual blind spots a great deal harder. But it can be done if you remain alert to the mental processes by which you arrived at a particular choice or solution.

Ask yourself – why do I think that to be true? On what are my conclusions based? How might the same object, situation or circumstance look if viewed from another angle?

Four – Search for causes; be sensitive to implications
One afternoon in 1941 Alexander Fleming was working in his London laboratory when he noticed that some of the bacteria which he was attempting to cultivate on jelly had died in the presence of dust spots. He might have simply discarded the spoiled plates and tried again – in which case he would not have discovered penicillin. Because he was alert to the implications of the setback, and exercised his curiosity, the world's first antibiotic was developed.

Five – Be open to new experiences
Keep on taking in new information, from books, newspapers and magazines, radio and TV shows. Don't get stuck in a rut and dismiss something new merely because it is new, original and not part of your previous experience. Somebody once said of the theatre-going public that they might not know what they like, but they nearly always like what they know! Avoid this trap. Listen carefully when a new idea is presented. When turning it over in your mind, or discussing it with others, adopt the PIN approach.

First find something *P*ositive to say. Do this before anything else. Almost every scheme, no matter how wildly improbable it may seem at first glance, has something good in it – maybe not a fully developed idea, but nearly always the germ of a bright idea.

Only when you have identified all its positive features should you consider any *I*nteresting aspects. These need not be positive, but they should be stimulating, new or in some other way worthy of your attention.

Finally, after all the Positive and Interesting points have been found and explored, you look at the *N* of the PIN approach and spend time on the proposal's truly *N*egative features.

By using PIN you'll make sure that good ideas, your own

or others', get a fair hearing and that your brain's capacity for analytical reasoning and critical judgement is fully exploited.

Six – Beware of conformity

A major barrier to effective thinking, this tends to loom larger as we grow older and develop a more cautious, conservative approach to life. Anthropologist Ashley Montague has called this process psychosclerosis, or hardening of the categories.

Place a pike in a tank full of minnows, and you'll soon be left with just the pike. Protect the minnows by placing them inside a glass jar within the tank, and you'll get a frustrated fish who spends a lot of time banging its nose on the glass walls in an attempt to grab a snack. But, after a while, even the pike learns that there's a barrier to his feeding and gives up. Now remove the protecting jar and a curious thing happens. The pike no longer even attempts to eat the minnows, who can swim right past its jaws in perfect safety. Biologists call this a signal reaction. The pike, having convinced itself that minnows can't be eaten, conforms to this belief even when the situation changes.

Many people conform for the same reasons. They replace active thinking with a reflex response based on past experiences.

I call these situations 'grabbers' because that's what they do – they grab your attention to the point where you don't notice anything else. Do you react in a knee-jerk manner to certain people, objects or circumstances? For instance, some people are so certain they'll never understand how to handle a piece of new technology that their eyes glaze over and they switch off before even bothering to give themselves a chance to make sense of the machine.

Other common 'grabbers' include bad language, sex education, doing maths, law and order, corporal punishment, blood sports, communism, socialism, conservatism, liberals, homosexuals, drug-takers, capitalism, religion and race. These words alone are enough to trigger a reflex response in some people based on conformity to a particular attitude of mind rather than an objective consideration of the evidence presented.

Always ask yourself, 'How do I know what I believe to be true?' There will be three possibilities. From experience, from observation and from reports prepared by others. All are subject to considerable bias, distortion and misinformation.

Martin knows from experience that Christmas has always been a major Christian festival. But he is wrong. In seventeenth-century Britain and colonial New England it was banned by the Puritans as a pagan feast. Christmas didn't become a legal holiday in Massachusetts until the mid nineteenth-century.

Observations are corrupted by prejudice, stereotyping and preconceptions.

Finally we have reports prepared by others, major sources being books, newspapers and TV. Misinformation, often of horrendous proportions, is propagated daily, either through carelessness, inadvertence or from a deliberate desire to mislead through the media. There is a feeling among many politicians, journalists, advertisers and public relations consultants, and anybody else with strongly held views to promote, that, in the words of American humorist Josh Billings, 'Honesty is the best policy in the long run, but for the short distances humbug has made pretty good time.'

This is not to say that you must disbelieve all you read, but that you should beware of conforming too readily to attitudes, ideas or opinions, no matter how widely held. As author William Drummond rightly said, 'He who will not reason is a bigot; he who cannot is a fool; he who dares not is a slave.'

Seven – Always think adaptively, never mechanically
When confronted by intellectual challenges many people seek sanctuary in certainty. They try and banish the anxiety aroused by having to solve problems and make decisions by becoming more and more sure of less and less. In the end they may be reduced to the condition of Pavlov's dogs,

except that instead of salivating in anticipation of meat they respond to any demand for thought with mental knee-jerks.

To every question they have an answer – neat, orderly, specific and almost invariably wrong. They are suffering from a condition known as mechanical thinking. This can afflict the brain at any age, although the risk rises with the passing of time. Its symptoms include the belief that one's attitudes, opinions and abilities are all fully formed and will not need to be changed again. Their outlook is rigid, unquestioning and limiting. The mechanical thinker rarely seeks for new information, hates changing his mind, prefers to have all questions neatly answered, all issues settled, all points decided – and always as simply as possible. They use absolute, all-or-nothing terms such as right – wrong, good – bad, success – failure. They are creatures of habit – social, physical and mental.

Such people pride themselves on their commonsense, a way of thinking which Einstein dismissed as the sum total of all the prejudices and misconceptions acquired by the age of eighteen, and novelist Herman Wouk describes as 'stupidity hardened into habit'. Such thinkers are not only highly conformist, they are also extremely easy to manipulate and control.

Develop the skills of adaptive thinking. Continually explore and experiment. Ask many questions and value knowledge for its own sake. Be prepared to change your mind, abandon opinions when found to be in error or facts if shown to be false. Be willing to tolerate shades of grey in life rather than seeking the reassuring, but deceptive, certainties of black and white.

Food for thought

To work properly your brain must be provided with exactly the right proportions and concentrations of a wide range of substances, including nutrients and oxygen. Even a moderate deficiency of B12 (cobalamin), for instance, can lead to mental illness.

There is evidence that increasing your intake of some

vitamins, as recommended in the next chapter, can help you think more efficiently. For instance, a relationship has been found between the amount of vitamin C ingested and results of intelligence tests.

In a 1960 study by A.L. Kubala and M.M. Katz, reported in the *Journal of Genetic Psychology*, children were divided into two groups according to the levels of ascorbic acid in their blood plasma. The highest scores were achieved by the group with high ascorbic acid levels. After both groups had been given daily drinks of fresh orange juice for six months, the blood plasma levels were equalised and the difference in test results disappeared.

Maximum mental ability was attained at a blood plasma level of 1.55mg of ascorbic acid per 100 millilitres of blood plasma. An eleven-stone man could achieve this level from a daily allowance of no more than 180mg of vitamin C. Commenting on this research in his book *How To Live Longer and Feel Better*, Linus Pauling concludes that, for peak mental performance, 'the daily allowance of ascorbic acid should be at least three times the 60mg recommended by the US Food and Nutrition Board and at least nine times the 20mg recommended by the corresponding British authority. Still larger intakes might have additional effect.'

Iron is also important for intellectual function. Measurements of electrical activity in the brain indicate that an insufficiency of iron results in lower levels of alertness. Pre-menopausal women are especially likely to experience such deficits, due to monthly blood loss. Studies suggest that as many as one-third may suffer in this way. Other groups who have been found to be at risk are male teenagers and people aged over sixty. Why iron depletion should be linked to a lack of alertness is not entirely clear. Research using animals has indicated that having too little iron in the system allows lead and cadmium, both toxins known to damage mental efficiency, to accumulate in the body.

Environmental lead comes from car exhausts, paint, industrial pollution and the sealants used on certain cans. Cadmium is present in drinking water which has passed through galvanised pipes, cigarette smoke, vegetables grown in cadmium-rich soil, many processed foods, plastic and other sources in the environment.

In addition to those supplements recommended in Chapter Eight you may find it useful to increase the amount of a neurotransmitter called acetylcholine (ACh) in your brain. This nerve-cell messenger, which among other functions regulates emotions, sexual drive and the waking/sleeping balance, is manufactured by the brain from two substances – choline and lecithin, which also contains choline in the form of phosphatidyl choline.

Choline is obtained from diet, and fish is a rich source. But there is evidence that boosting the input of either choline or lecithin can enhance mental performance. In an experiment conducted by the US National Institute for Mental Health, volunteers who took 10 grams of choline chloride showed a significant improvement in retention and recall when tested ninety minutes later. Those with the poorest memories prior to taking the choline showed the most marked improvements. Similar results were obtained by researchers at MIT when students given 3 grams of choline per day proved better at learning lists of words and had enhanced general recall.

The type sold in many health-food shops, choline bitartate, has a tendency to cause diarrhoea, a side-effect avoided when choline chloride (also known as choline hydrochloride) is substituted. The problem with taking choline in the latter form is that it is poorly digested, being converted by the intestinal bacteria to triethylamine, a substance with a distinctly unpleasant fishy odour. If this happens, try altering your intestinal bacteria by taking yoghurt or increasing the fibre in your diet.

An alternative is to take your choline in the form of lecithin, a nutrient present in many foodstuffs including calf's liver (850mg per 100 grams), soya beans (1,480mg), wheatgerm (2,820mg) and peanuts (1,113mg).

Lecithin can be purchased from health-food stores and many chemists. It may be obtained either as capsules or granules which can be spread on cereals, taken in liquid or swallowed off the spoon. Purchase only lecithin composed of phosphatidyl choline, since other forms contain impurities and provide less choline per dose. The taste is bland and slightly fatty, but not unpleasant.

However, there is a difficulty in deriving your choline from this source. Research suggests that some people will require a fairly large amount of choline, at least 10 grams per day, to get any significant benefit. To obtain 10 grams of choline you must consume 30 grams of lecithin and its high fat content (there are 9 calories in each gram) could lead to unwanted weight gain.

My advice is to experiment with various doses of choline and see what level of dose is needed to improve memory and make you feel more alert. If the smell proves a problem, and the ideas suggested above don't provide the answer, then switch to lecithin – I prefer the granules – and, once again, try out various levels of consumption.

With sound nutrition, exercise and the procedures for stimulating your brain suggested above there should be no decline in either intellectual agility or ability with the passing of time. But just as it is essential to make muscles work in order to preserve their strength and tone, so too is it vital that you keep your mind hard at work.

By learning poetry or prose passages on a regular basis you can continue to enjoy rapid retention and accurate recall to the very end of your life. By giving your powers of problem-solving, judgement, critical reasoning and logical deduction frequent work-outs you'll be certain of maintaining them at maximum. By using your talents for imagination, innovation, invention, curiosity and creativity on a daily basis you'll keep these essential mind skills in prime condition.

With intellectual skills as with physical fitness the choice is a simple one. You either use them or you lose them.

Eight: Vitamin power

'First a new theory is attacked as absurd.
Then it is admitted to be true but
insignificant. Finally it is seen to be so
important that its adversaries claim that they
themselves discovered it.'

(William James)

So far we have concentrated on the psychological aspects of
aging. Now we must turn from mind to body and consider
ways in which, by minimising wear and tear on the cells,
our rate of physical degeneration can be slowed down. In
this quest for a long and healthy life some of our most
potent allies are vitamins.

The word vitamin, which was first coined in 1912, means
'life-giving nitrogen compound'. Although the chemistry
turned out to be incorrect, the name perfectly reflects the
central role of vitamins in survival. Without small amounts of
these vital organic substances, metabolism could not occur,
damaged cells would never be repaired or worn-out ones
replaced. As we shall see, even a minor deficiency can result
in potentially fatal consequences.

Yet, remarkably, our body can neither store some of the
vitamins most crucial to health nor manufacture them, either
at all or in sufficient quantities to meet our needs. So to stay
healthy we must obtain sufficient amounts of many vitamins
from our diet, or provide the body with raw materials to
produce those it can manufacture from the food we eat. The
question is . . .

How much is enough?
While no doctor or dietitian disputes the need for a recommended minimum daily allowance (RDA) of vitamins, there

are serious differences of opinion over the value of taking them in amounts far larger than are necessary to avoid deficiency diseases.

Some experts still insist that a properly balanced diet provides all that is needed for good health. When vitamins are consumed in large quantities, they claim, you simply produce expensive urine! The view expressed by Dr Vernon Coleman in his book *Body Sense*, that 'more nonsense is talked about vitamins than any other foodstuffs' undoubtedly reflects the views of many physicians. Vernon Coleman goes on to assert that the benefits claimed by advocates of mega-vitamin therapy are either untrue or 'based on flimsy, disputable or rocky evidence'.

Those who have devoted a lifetime to the study of vitamin therapy would, not surprisingly, strongly dispute such contemptuous dismissal of their research. Professor Linus Pauling, twice a Nobel laureate and probably the most eminent advocate of vitamin C as a means of combating a range of diseases from cancer to the common cold, insists that:

> You can, by taking some simple and inexpensive measures, lead a longer life and extend your years of well-being. My most important recommendation is that you take vitamins every day in optimum amounts . . . those optimum amounts are much larger than the minimum supplemental intake usually recommended by physicians and old-fashioned nutritionists.

If you embark on the vitamin procedures contained in the FAR programme, it is likely that you will meet scepticism and criticisms along the lines I've described. In this chapter I shall be describing the functions of the vitamins which are included in the FAR programme, explaining which foodstuffs contain them and looking at the results of deficiencies. I shall also be giving the RDA alongside the doses required to facilitate active regeneration. I shall not, however, be providing a detailed refutation of the criticisms levelled against vitamin therapy nor describing the evidence in its support. Those interested in learning what science has discovered about the benefits of mega-vitamins – and, far from being 'flimsy, disputable or rocky', the findings are massive, convincing and detailed – will find references in the bibliography.

But while scientific data provide invaluable support for the importance of mega-multi-vitamins in the pursuit of healthy longevity, the most convincing arguments are to be found in personal experience.

I suggest, therefore, that you keep an open mind on the subject and follow the plan suggested by your assessment results and described at the end of this chapter. If, after six months, you have not observed any difference in your physical and emotional health, stamina, energy levels and resistance to infection, then you won't need any encouragement to abandon this aspect of the FAR programme.

However, if, as I firmly believe, you find that the additional vitamins and minerals have made a substantial difference to your well-being, then you will not require the results of clinical studies to continue with the programme.

The meaning of mega-vitamins

When doctors claim that our food provides all necessary vitamins, what they mean is that you are not going to succumb to a deficiency-related disease. Your gums won't bleed from scurvy, you will escape the muscle weakness of beriberi, and the bone deformities of rickets.

As I shall explain in the next chapter, a proper diet is extremely important, not only to one's general health but also as part of the FAR programme. Only by ensuring that your body has the essential building blocks of proteins, carbohydrates and fats can strength, stamina and vitality be sustained. Furthermore, the effective absorption of vitamins detailed in the FAR programme depends on a well-balanced diet, a point which I shall be considering later in this chapter.

But even when such a diet is followed and the RDA met, the level of vitamin intake will still fall below the consumption advocated by mega-multi-vitamin therapy. The size of this discrepancy for just three vitamins is given in Table 4 opposite.

Table 4

Vitamin	Recommended daily intake	FAR programme vitamin levels
B1	1.5mg	75–500mg
B2	1.2mg	75–300mg
C	60mg	1–6g

Some people believe they are doing all that is necessary by swallowing a multi-vitamin tablet each day. But a single tablet comes nowhere near to providing the amounts required for FAR. One popular brand, for example, contains only 150mg of vitamin C.

When you consider that a 6-oz glass of concentrated fruit juice provides some 300mg, and the FAR programme suggests up to 6 grams per day, it becomes clear how small a contribution such tablets make. Where multi-vitamins do have a valuable role to play, especially when taken in therapeutic strength (they are labelled as such), is in maintaining a balance between the vitamins.

No one vitamin, or group of vitamins, is more or less important than others. Nor – with one exception – does it matter whether they are labelled 'natural' or not. A vitamin is a vitamin no matter how it has been produced.

But don't make the mistake of seeing mega-multivitamins as an alternative to sensible eating. As I have explained, and will describe further in the next chapter, appropriate nutrition is just as much an essential component of Facilitated Active Regeneration as exercise and a positive mental approach to life.

The role of vitamins in your life

Let's now consider the main vitamins which you will be taking when following the FAR programme. Before discussing them, it may be helpful to describe the various ways in which vitamins are measured.

Measures of vitamin strength

Vitamins A, D, E, F and K are fat-soluble, which means they are absorbed through the digestive tract and may be stored in the tissues. They are normally measured in international units or IUs. New measurements have also been introduced for vitamins A and E; these too will be described in the appropriate sections.

Water-soluble vitamins, the B group and C, are taken in through the digestive tract and transported around the body in the blood. They cannot be stored by the body and must be provided as needed, either directly from the diet or – in the case of the B group only – by being manufactured in the body. These are measured in grams (1 oz = 28.4 grams), milligrams (1/1000th gram, abbreviated mg) and micrograms (1/1,000,000th gram, abbreviated mcg).

Vitamin A – retinol

RDA: 5,000 IUs or 1500 RE.

FAR recommended range: 10–20,000 IUs or 6–12,000 RE per day. (*Note*: 1 IU = 0.6mcg beta-carotene. RE stands for a new measure of potency *retinol equivalents*. 1 RE = 3.33 IUs retinol or 10 IUs beta-carotene.)

Toxic level: above 80,000 IUs per day for adults and above 15,000 for children. Do *not* exceed the maximum dose suggested above.

What it does

Vitamin A is a fat-soluble nutrient which acts as a powerful antioxidant and protector against the scourge of free radicals. Its name retinol is derived from its role in maintaining the light-sensitive layer at the back of the eye, the retina. A close relation of retinol is carotenoid. As its name suggests, the best source of this is carrots, whose pigment is produced by beta-carotene. It is called a pro-vitamin because the body uses it to synthesise the vitamin itself.

One of the key building blocks of sound health, Vitamin A is essential for the maintenance of night vision, skin tissue, the mucous membranes (which line the mouth, throat, respiratory passages and urinary tract) and the normal development of bones. It aids the healing of wounds, protects the system during periods of stress and can detoxify certain poisons. A deficiency can lead to excessive menstruation and male infertility. It can also damage one's hearing by reducing the amount of mucous in the inner ear.

This mucous protects the ear by trapping bacteria, dirt and dust, and passing it into the mouth, via the Eustachian tubes, where the muck can be swallowed and disposed of. Vitamin A also safeguards the sensory mechanisms of the inner ear and is implicated in our sense of smell.

Because a healthy mucous membrane also protects the mouth, throat and lungs vitamin A deficiency can reduce the protection afforded against respiratory-tract infections such as colds and sinus problems.

Recently, French doctors have reported that vitamin A also enhances resistance to infections in general. A study of the relationship between nutrition and health in 100 people aged over sixty showed that concentrations of vitamin A in the blood plasma correlated with the body's ability to produce antigens, the cells which fight infections. High levels of antigens were associated with high levels of vitamin A. It helps keep the epithelial cells which line our gut healthy, promotes the growth of sound teeth and protects them from dental decay (caries).

The role of vitamin A in night vision lies in the production of a substance called visual purple in the retina. Early indications that there is a deficiency of this vitamin in the diet are night blindness and discomfort when trying to work for any length of time in bright lights. A driver suffering from a lack of vitamin A, for instance, would be easily dazzled by approaching headlamps. If your job involves working for long periods under strong illumination (as in fine assembly work, television or film production, or even writing by the light of a desk lamp for several hours each day) or if you live by the sea or in the mountains, your vitamin A requirements will increase.

Another common indication of a deficiency is bad dandruff or a poor complexion as dead cells clog up the pores, producing blackheads and pimples. Heavy drinkers are at special risk of eye damage, because alcohol interferes with the liver's ability to store and release the vitamin.

It has also been found that the production of RNA, which as you will remember from the previous chapter is the cell's working blueprint, is proportional to the amount of vitamin A in the liver.

From this short outline of the vitamin's multiplicity of essential roles in the body, it is apparent that many of the degenerative symptoms which occur in the aging disease, from worsening eyesight, loss of hearing and taste to the inefficient functioning of cells, may be attributable to deficiencies of this vitamin.

A high *positive* score on statements **8,9,16** and **17** of Assessment One could indicate a deficiency of vitamin A in your diet.

As you read through the section below, you should consider how many of the foodstuffs listed form part of your daily diet.

Vitamin A and the food you eat
As a rough guide, the deeper the yellow pigmentation of a fruit or vegetable the more beta-carotene it contains. The different amounts present in six common foods are shown below.

Table 5

Foodstuff per 100 grams	Carotenoid values in IUs
Green beans	300
Peas	400
Fresh apricots	3,000
Raw carrots	8,000

One of the richest sources is liver, whether from animals or fish.

The vitamin survives cooking at normal temperatures and can be canned without significant loss of potency. The level of vitamin A in a tin of carrots canned in 1824 was as high when the can was opened over 110 years later. However, it is vulnerable to oxidation and destruction when the fats containing it go rancid. When milk is processed much of its vitamin A is destroyed by the action of oxygen. It is also destroyed by sunlight, so take your milk indoors as quickly as possible on sunny days, and avoid buying sun-dried apricots or jars of pickled herrings which have been displayed in the shop window.

The totals given in food tables should be treated with caution since these are usually an ideal, or possible maximum, rather than a guaranteed quantity. As vitamin specialist Dr Michael Colgan points out, there can be considerable variations in the amount of vitamin A present in foods reputedly high in this nutrient. In carrots the quantity can range from a low of 70 to a high of 18,500 IUs, while liver may contain as little as 470 IUs per 100 grams or as much as 41,200.

Raw vegetables are not necessarily a better source of the vitamin than those which have been cooked properly. If you eat raw carrots, for example, only about 1 per cent of their carotene will be absorbed during digestion for conversion into vitamin A. This is because the carotene is contained within the cellulose walls of the plant's cells, and these walls cannot be broken down by the human digestive tract. Since vitamin A is fat – not water – soluble it does not pass through the cell walls. Grating or chopping carrots and then boiling them breaks down the cellulose barriers and liberates the carotene. It can also be extracted by liquidising. But if you do this be sure to drink the raw juice immediately after preparation or the vitamin A will be destroyed by oxygen.

The risks of vitamin A
Every few years there are reports of people being poisoned by excessive dosages of this vitamin. In 1974, for example, critics of vitamin supplements used the death of a forty-eight-year-old vitamin A addict named Basil Brown to 'demonstrate' their supposed dangers. Ten years later, the *New York Times* described how a child had been rushed to hospital with headache, dehydration, vomiting and pains in her arms and legs after taking an overdose.

In every case the amounts consumed have been far in excess of anything suggested by those advocating supplementary vitamin A. Basil Brown, for example, had taken 33 million IUs over a ten-day period, in addition to drinking eight pints of freshly prepared carrot juice a day. Not surprisingly, his liver collapsed under this assault. The child had swallowed 200,000 IUs a day for three months. The RDA for a child that age is 2,500 IUs, or half the adult allowance.

Because it is fat-soluble, vitamin A can build up in the body and reach a level where it produces headaches (due to raised pressure inside the skull), impairment of vision, nosebleeds and tenderness of the joints. However, the daily dosage necessary to achieve such levels is at least 100,000 IUs taken over a period of twelve months or longer. The dosage advocated in the FAR programme is perfectly safe. You must not, however, be tempted to exceed it. Nor is it advisable to eat foodstuffs rich in vitamin A such as kidneys, herrings and mackerel several times in the same week.

Vitamin D – calciferol
RDA: 400 IUs.
  FAR recommended range: 400–600 IUs per day.
  Measurement standard: 1 IU vitamin D = 0.025mcg pure vitamin D.
  Toxic level: above 30,000 IUs per day for adults and 2,000 for children. Rarely, people show symptoms of poisoning at 5,000 IUs. Do not exceed the maximum dose given above and then take only in conjunction with the diet procedures described in the next chapter.

What it does
Another fat-soluble vitamin, its main function is regulating calcium and phosphate metabolism. It is essential for the building of healthy bones and teeth. Deficiencies result in rickets, as already noted, as well as severe inflammation of the gums (pyorrhoea alveolaris), a thinning and weakening of the bones (osteoporosis), retarded growth and lack of vigour.

Vitamin D and the food you eat
It can be produced in the skin through the action of sunlight. Foods rich in D include fish, especially herrings, kippers, tuna, mackerel, pilchards, sardines or bloaters. Liver, egg yolk and butter are other sources.

As noted above, vitamin D, like A, can be harmful if taken in excessive amounts and the maximum stated in the FAR programme should not be exceeded. A toxic dose will produce weakness, nausea, diarrhoea, raised blood pressure and impaired kidney function among other symptoms. Similar problems can be encountered at a dose as low as 4,000 IUs when taken on a regular basis.

In supplements the vitamin is usually supplied as D2 (ergocalciferol) or D3 (cholecalciferol) and only in conjunction with vitamin A or as part of a multi-vitamin.

Vitamin E – tocopherol
RDA: 10 IUs.

FAR recommended range: 500–1,000 IUs per day.

Measurement standard: 1 IU vitamin E = 1mg alpha-tocopherol. In the US a new standard has just been adopted and may appear on supplement content labels. This is a measure in milligram equivalents of alpha-tocopherol activity (TE). 1mg d-alpha-tocopherol = 1 alpha TE. As with the new way of measuring vitamin A, you need not concern yourself overmuch with this change. It is described here for the sake of completeness and to prevent bafflement if you suddenly find TE on a supplement listing.

The 'd' in d-alpha-tocopherol refers to the dextro form which is present in nature. Synthetic vitamin E contains both dextro and levo alpha-tocopherol which cannot be utilised by the body. Make sure you purchase the 'd' form – which will probably be more expensive than the 'dl' type – since this is cheaper to manufacture. Always buy it fresh and use it rapidly since oxidation occurs within a few months of manufacture.

Toxic level: none known. But at levels above 1,200 IUs per day it sometimes raises already high blood pressure and can also affect diabetes patients and those with thyroid disorders.

If you suffer from hypertension, diabetes or thyroid disorders, seek advice from your doctor before taking this vitamin.

What it does
Discovered in 1922 by Herbert M. Evans, professor of biochemistry at the University of California, and his co-worker Katherine Scott Bishop, this vitamin occurs as a family of substances called tocopherols. These include alpha, beta, delta and gamma-tocopherols. Since all have different activity levels, vitamin E is measured in IUs rather than milligrams.

As I explained in Chapter Five, vitamin E is a powerful, natural anti-cross-linking agent (ACLA) which helps to safeguard the integrity of the cells, especially their outer membranes, from damage by free radicals.

Because it can easily be stored by the body in large quantities, a dietary deficiency can continue for some considerable time before any adverse physical effects become apparent. However, once it has been depleted, the body's store rebuilds very slowly, so that a severe deficit may not be made good for a lengthy period after the basic minimum allowance is restored.

Vitamin E has been found to lower the amounts of HDL cholesterol –(see p. 49) in the bloodstream, so reducing the risk of arteriosclerosis. It removes toxins from the blood, so improving the transportation of oxygen and enhancing muscle health. For example, patients who had suffered major heart attacks were found to show a marked strength-ening of the heart muscles following daily supplements of 1,500 IUs.

Burns and open wounds heal more rapidly, with supplements as low as 600 IUs producing marked re-ductions in healing time and less scar tissue. People suffering from muscle weakness or stiffness in the joints have reported an improvement on a daily dose of 400 IUs. Vitamin E also has a role to play in male fertility by in-creasing the number and motility of the sperm.

Vitamin E and the food you eat
The tocopherols are present in leafy green vegetables, such

as cabbage and lettuce, wheatgerm, whole grains, vegetable oils and nuts. Wheatgerm oil is the most commonly used source of vitamin E in supplements. It is destroyed when the food is heated while exposed to air, frozen or stored for long periods. During frying in oil 98 per cent is lost. It is also removed when grains are refined or if food is allowed to go rancid. It has been estimated that since we started refining grains our daily intake of this vitamin from foods has fallen to around 8 IUs.

Vitamins K and F
Although just as important to healthy growth as the other vitamins, these may be obtained in adequate amounts by adopting the diet procedures relating to fats which are fully described in the next chapter.

From fat-soluble vitamins we move to the B group and vitamin C, which are all water-soluble.

The B group of vitamins
There is a greater chance of deficiencies occuring within this group than with any of the other vitamins. It has been estimated that up to 70 per cent of the populations of Europe and the USA suffer such deficits as a result of the refining of grains and sugar. Until the nineteenth century, bread was made from wholewheat grain, while sweetening came from molasses, a form of sugar rich in B vitamins. Today, as much as two-thirds of our daily calories are provided by foods which have been largely, or entirely, stripped of their natural B vitamins. While some of these are, it is true, replaced by the manufacturers, such 'enrichment' replaces only a small part of what has been removed.

Thanks to the activity of bacteria working away in our intestines we are able to produce our own B group vitamins, providing our diets contain milk sugar (lactose) and fat, which are the raw materials on which intestinal bacteria go to work. Yoghurt is valuable to health in many ways, not least because it is rich in B-vitamin-producing bacteria that can live in the gut. Because these bacteria are destroyed by antibiotics, it's important to increase your consumption of B vitamins should your doctor ever place you on a course of these drugs.

All the B vitamins are water-soluble and cannot be stored by the body. It is essential, therefore, to ensure that your diet contains the raw materials from which this group can be synthesised.

Vitamin B1 – thiamine
RDA: 1.5mg.

FAR recommended range: 75–500mg per day.

Toxic level: none known. It colours your urine bright yellow but this is quite harmless.

What it does
Beriberi, whose symptoms include paralysis and numbness, respiratory and heart failure, occurs when the intake of B1 (thiamine) is too low. It was only in 1886 that a Dutch physician, Christiaan Eijkman, found a direct link between the disease and diet. He observed that chickens fed polished rice, from which the husks had been removed, showed symptoms closely resembling those of beriberi. It was the casually discarded husks which contained the precious B1.

Thiamine has a crucial role in breaking down carbohydrates to produce energy. Although the substantial deficits which result in beriberi are rarely found in the developed countries, less severe deficiencies are fairly common as a result of food-processing and incorrect cooking. Like all members of this group, the fact that B1 is water-soluble means that it can easily be washed out of foods during preparation.

Even a mild deficiency makes it impossible for the cells to function with maximum efficiency since they become clogged with pyruvic acid, a by-product of energy production, and are unable to take up oxygen. This leads to a rapid loss of energy and mental alertness, bringing about feelings of lethargy, depression and fatigue. The most affected organs are the heart, brain, nervous system and digestive tract.

Because B1 has gained a reputation of being an 'energy' vitamin some people are tempted to take it alone as a dietary supplement. *This is harmful and to be avoided* since all the vitamins in this group must work together in order to be effective.

Vitamin B1 and the food you eat
The major natural sources of this vitamin are wheatgerm, cereal grains, nuts, dried beans, peas, soya, lentils, peanut butter, breads baked from wholewheat, rice bran, yeast and yeast extracts, milk, eggs, kidneys, lean pork, liver, bacon and fresh red meat.

Vitamin B2 – riboflavin
RDA: 1.2mg.
   FAR recommended range: 75–300mg per day.
   Toxic level: none known. As with thiamine, however, it turns urine yellow.

What it does
Riboflavin is essential for the production of enzymes which metabolise proteins, carbohydrates and fats. It also neutralises the acidity resulting from the burning of nutrients to release energy. B2 combines with oxygen to nourish the cells of the cornea, the eye's protective covering, and so plays a key part in vision. Deficiencies result in poor eyesight, especially under low light levels, and the eyes may hurt when exposed to very bright lights. People suffering from this deficiency often need to wear dark glasses even on dull days. The eyes become itchy and bloodshot with an increasing risk of cataracts developing when the deficit is long-lasting.

   The complexion is poor. There can be eczema, and whiteheads sometimes form beneath the skin, which may also become highly coloured in appearance, due to dilation of the capillaries. The tongue may take on a purple hue, the lips crack and develop sores, especially at the corners. The hair looks dull and oily.

Vitamin B2 and the food you eat
The richest source of riboflavin is liver, 100 grams of lambs'
liver contain around 5mg of B2. Eggs and yeast are also rich
in B2. Milk is a poor source because the vitamin is destroyed
by ultraviolet light, which means that only a short exposure
on the doorstep can greatly reduce the B2 content. Yoghurt
supplies both B2 and B6 in addition to essential amino-acids
and, as noted above, the bacteria which allow the body to
manufacture all the B group vitamins.

Much of the riboflavin in vegetables is lost during cooking,
being discarded with the water used for boiling.

Vitamin B3 – niacin, nicotinic acid, niacinamide

RDA: 10mg.

FAR recommended range: 75–500mg per day.

Toxic level: it has very low toxicity and even doses as high
as 2,000mg can be consumed for long periods without harm.
If you have a peptic ulcer or suffer from diabetes consult your
doctor first, since the vitamin can have side effects in such
cases. Niacin and nicotinic acid occasionally cause slight skin
irritation, which quickly disappears. However, you may prefer to use the niacinamide form which has no such effect.

What it does
B3 is present in every cell of the body. It is involved in
metabolism and the regulation of blood sugar and histamine
levels. It also reduces levels of cholesterol. A major role is in
brain function, with deficiencies resulting in memory loss,
depression, insomnia, increasing irritability and a general
decline in intellectual capacity. Mild deficiencies produce
mouth sores, a coated tongue and unpleasant oral odour.
People experiencing a significant niacin deficit become tense
and nervous. Large doses of B3, together with vitamin C,
have been used in the successful treatment of schizophrenia.

Other complaints in which niacin has proved effective include arteriosclerosis, arthritis, acne, depression and, of
course, pellagra. You should increase your B3 intake at times
of special emotional stress. Your need for extra niacin is

suggested by a high positive score on statements **1, 2, 3, 5** or **10** of Assessment Two.

Vitamin B3 and the food you eat
It is present in yeast, peanuts, poultry, wheatgerm, liver, kidneys, muscle meats, fish, eggs, wholemeal cereals and dried fruits.

Vitamin B5 – pantothenic acid
RDA: not yet established.
  FAR recommended range: 75–500mg per day.
  Toxic level: none known.

What it does
The name of this vitamin comes from the Greek 'pantos' meaning everywhere; this reflects both its widespread distribution in foodstuffs and the tremendous number of roles it plays in our body. B5 is involved in energy production, the synthesis of cholesterol and fat, the formation of antibodies in the immune system and the manufacture of transmitter substances for the nervous system. It strengthens the adrenal glands, improving cortisone production and enhancing resistance to stress. It has been used successfully in the treatment of arthritis and rheumatism. B5 is also involved in the production of several hormones, including the male sex hormone testosterone.

A serious and prolonged deficiency leads to rapid fatigue, a desire to sleep a great deal, constipation, loss of appetite, irritability, baldness and a lowered resistance to infectious diseases. Other symptoms include headaches, dizziness, muscle cramps, rapid heartbeat and lowered blood pressure. Pantothenic acid provides protection against common infections, especially colds and other upper respiratory-tract infections.

Vitamin B5 and the food you eat
Despite the fact that it is found so widely in foodstuffs, deficiencies can still occur in people who eat large quantities of processed foods, and it is readily destroyed by

canning or over-cooking. B5 occurs in yeast, wheatgerm, wheat bran, wholegrain bread and cereals, green vegetables, and in kidneys, liver and heart.

Vitamin B6 – pyridoxine
RDA: 2mg.

FAR recommended range: 75–400mg per day.

Toxic level: none established. However, you should not exceed the maximum given above since effects above this level have not been fully investigated. Excessive dosage may lead to disturbed sleep and very vivid dreams.

What it does
The list of this vitamin's vital functions seems almost endless. It helps regulate the sodium/potassium balance essential for an effectively functioning system, makes antibodies, is necessary for the absorption of B12 (see below), manufactures hormones, enzymes and transmitters for the nervous system. It is required for the metabolism of protein, carbohydrate and fat. It has been found effective in the treatment of post-natal depression, digestive disorders and kidneystones. A natural analgesic, it can be used to relieve pain.

The first symptoms of B6 deficiency are headaches, nervousness and an inability to concentrate. The sufferer becomes irritable and suspicious, suffers from dizzy spells, feels sick and may vomit. Their complexion is poor and they may have bad dandruff.

Adequate B6 is essential during pregnancy, when it can relieve muscle cramps and nausea.

Vitamin B6 and the food you eat
Like all B group vitamins, pyridoxine is easily lost by overcooking, canning, long storage and exposure to light. Fish, wheatgerm, yeast and walnuts are the best natural sources.

Vitamin B12 – cobalamins
RDA: 3mcg.
  FAR recommended range: 10–100mcg per day.
  Toxic level: none known.

What it does
This vitamin comprises several different substances, all of which contain cobalt – hence the name. It works in conjunction with folic acid (see below) to promote cell division, improve RNA function, build proteins and ensure the health of red blood cells. Because so little is required for normal functioning – the RA is after all only 3 millionths of a gram – deficiencies are very rare among people who eat animal proteins, which are the sole source of this vitamin. It can, however, pose a problem for vegans.

A more common cause of deficiency is a failure of the body to absorb B12 once ingested. For absorption to take place the gastric juices must contain an 'intrinsic factor'. In its absence, no amount of the vitamin in the stomach is going to safeguard you against a deficiency. This can occur in people who have had surgery to treat, for instance, stomach ulcers or who are taking some kinds of prescribed medication. A link has also been reported between low levels of B12 and taking oral contraceptives.

Deficiencies have the most serious consequences for cells which divide rapidly, such as those manufacturing blood in the bone marrow or in the testes. Lower sperm counts have been found in men who have a diet lacking animal protein. It can also produce deterioration in the nervous system and lead to stiffness of the joints and menstrual difficulties. An early indication of B12 deficiency is soreness of the mouth and tongue.

This vitamin is used in the treatment of anaemia, diabetes, multiple sclerosis and morning sickness.

Vitamin B12 and the food you eat
As I explained above, the vitamin is found only in animal proteins. Liver is an especially rich source but you can also find it in all meats, eggs, milk and other dairy products.

Folic acid
RDA: 400mcg.
　FAR recommended range 400–600mcg per day.
　Toxic level: none known.

What it does
As we have seen, folic acid works with B12 in all its functions.

Folic acid and the food you eat
The major natural sources are liver, yeast, nuts, legumes and raw, green, leafy vegetables. It is found in oranges and bananas but few other fruits. Folic acid is easily destroyed and much of it is lost when cooking water is discarded. It is also destroyed in the body by various drugs including sedatives.

Vitamin C – ascorbic acid
RDA: 60mg.
　FAR recommended range: 1–6 grams per day.
　Toxic level: none known. May cause slight diarrhoea when first taken due to its acidity, but the body soon adapts.

What it does
Scurvy, the scourge of navies ever since mankind embarked on long sea voyages, was finally defeated in 1747, when James Lind, a Scottish physician employed by the Royal Navy, demonstrated that it could be cured by including citrus fruits in the seamen's rations. Its cause was the absence of vitamin C from their diet of hard tack and salted meat.

　Whole books can, and have, been written about this single vitamin. There is only space here to describe a few of its vital functions and the protection it can provide against the aging disease. For those interested in learning more about it, I can recommend the books by its greatest advocate, Linus Pauling, which will be found in the reference section.

Vitamin C is unique in that it can be manufactured in the bodies of all animals except apes, guinea pigs, a species of Indian bat, certain oriental birds and human beings! One theory is that, because vitamin C could be obtained so easily from tropical plants and fruit at an early stage in mankind's evolutionary history, there was no reason for the body to devote effort and energy in manufacturing it from glucose. As a result, we lost this ability and must rely entirely on our diet for this water-soluble, and therefore non-storable, vitamin.

What it does
Vitamin C helps produce collagen, the body's intercellular glue which supports cartilage, skin, connective tissue and bones. It is essential to the healthy development of bones, cartilage and teeth. When taken in mega-doses it activates the white blood cells and acts as an anti-bacterial, anti-viral agent combating a wide range of infections and environmental pollutants. There is also good evidence that it assists in the destruction of cancerous tumours. A recent paper by the Australian Society of Epidemiology, for example, reported that large doses of vitamin C reduce the risk of rectal cancer.

Ascorbic acid has been found to lower levels of the hazardous LDL cholesterol in elderly male patients. One gram per day was capable of reducing LDL cholesterol levels by up to 15 per cent, according to a report in the *Lancet*.

In the University of Texas, male infertility problems resulting from the clumping together of sperms were successfully treated by means of a 1-gram daily dose of this vitamin.

One of its most important functions, is in the war against age-promoting free radicals. It safeguards other vitamins, and fatty acids, from destruction in the body by attaching itself to the damaging oxide and transporting it out of the system. It also frees the body of such toxins as mercury, carbon dioxide, DDT and lead.

Early symptoms of a deficiency are the ease with which the skin bruises and gums bleed, due to increased weakness of the fragile capillary walls. Tiny haemorrhages cause pain

in the intestines, bone marrrow and joints. A lack of this
vitamin during childhood results in stunted growth and
teeth especially vulnerable to decay. The bones of such
children are brittle and break easily. Such breaks take
longer to mend, while cuts and sores are slow to heal.
Deficiencies are most likely to be found during late adulthood (fifty years upwards) when the body's need for the
vitamin sharply rises. Interestingly, many of the symptoms
of the aging disease, such as wrinkled skin, tooth loss and
brittle bones, are identical with those seen in scurvy.

Vitamin C and the food you eat
Because it is so widely distributed in fresh fruits and
vegetables most people assume that they must be getting at
least the recommended daily allowance from their normal
diet. But this is not necessarily true. Where few fresh fruits or
vegetables are consumed, a deficiency can easily result. And
even where a substantial amount of these are eaten the wide
variations in amounts present, even in foods supposedly rich
in the vitamin, could still lead to a deficit. Dr Michael Colgan
has reported the following ranges of vitamin C in 100 grams
of the following fruit and vegetables. Quantities of vitamin C
found are given in milligrams:

Oranges (without skin)	Carrots (unpeeled)	Tomatoes (with skins)
trace – 116	1 – 8	9 –38

'The first oranges we tested,' he reports, 'were bought from
a local supermarket. Their vitamin C content was zero.
They looked, smelled and tasted perfectly normal. Probably
they had been stored for a long time.'

When he and his colleagues tested oranges bought
directly from a grower and picked that day, each orange
contained 180mg of vitamin C (116mg per 100 grams).

As these figures show, even foodstuffs which start out high
in vitamin C can lose most, if not all, of their ascorbic acid
by prolonged storage or transportation, poor canning or
careless preparation and cooking. Since it is water-soluble,

vitamin C is frequently poured down the drain after greens have been cooked. In living plants moisture speeds the vitamin's production, but after picking those same conditions hasten its destruction as oxidation attacks and destroys the ascorbic acid. Many drugs, including aspirin, destroy vitamin C in the body. Smokers, too, require more of the vitamin to combat toxins absorbed through their lungs and digestion.

Correct preparation and storage of food is essential if vitamin C is to be preserved. Freezing safeguards ascorbic acid, but any prolonged exposure to the air after thawing will destroy it. Vegetables should never be left exposed to the air for longer than is absolutely necessary after being peeled or chopped. Provided it has been properly canned and stored, tinned orange juice can be just as good a source as the juice of fresh oranges. However, since you can never be certain that the canning has been done efficiently, it is always better to squeeze your own juice from fresh oranges. If you do this be sure to include the pulp and white rind in your drink since these contain substances which aid absorption of the vitamin.

To obtain the large daily dose recommended in the FAR programme you should obtain vitamin C in powder form and then drink it in fruit juice. Stir into the juice and then allow to stand for ten minutes to ensure that it has completely dissolved. I suggest that you begin by taking your vitamin C at breakfast, but if this produces an upset stomach or loose bowel movements – which occasionally happens due to the acidity – try taking it later in the day. Drink the juice after eating food, rather than before or during, to cushion its effects. After a short time your body will become accustomed to the acidity and you should have no further difficulty.

A little sugar or glucose can be added to the juice, provided of course that you do not suffer from diabetes, to take the edge off the bitterness.

If you are diabetic, then remember that taking vitamin C will affect laboratory tests, so you should stop taking the supplement for two or three days before any such tests are to be made.

Getting the most from your vitamins

As important to Facilitated Active Regeneration as the mega-vitamins you take is the efficiency with which they are absorbed by the body. After all, there is little point in buying these essential nutrients merely to have them pass straight through your body and get flushed away. The extent to which a nutrient can be taken up by the body is termed bioavailability.

This is a complex process involving many different reactions and interactions, some of which enhance absorption while others inhibit it. In order to get the best from the vitamins suggested in the FAR programme you will need to prepare your body to receive them, by combining vitamins with more easily absorbed proteins.

Most of the foods we eat in bulk (macronutrients) consist of proteins, carbohydrates and fats, all of which have the capacity to interfere with our system's uptake of micronutrients in the form of vitamins and minerals.

When protein is eaten in excess – recent US figures showed daily consumption levels were twice what is necessary for good health – several minerals are less easily absorbed or utilised, while others are more readily excreted. Such a diet can, for instance, produce a calcium deficiency, so increasing the risk of kidney stones and osteoporosis (loss of calcium from the bones).

High-fibre diets, which include a great deal of raw bran, while health-promoting in many ways can also inhibit the absorption of minerals in the bowel. The most seriously affected are zinc and calcium, although iron, magnesium and other trace elements also bind in the fibres and are less easily taken up by the body.

To ensure maximum bioavailability of your vitamins, you should follow the diet suggestions in the next chapter. In addition take the following as supplements.

Zinc

RDA: 15mg.

FAR recommended supplement: 4–5mg per day.

Toxic levels: Do *not* go beyond the range given above,

since excess zinc competes with copper and may lead to a copper deficiency anaemia. It can also impair your ability to absorb calcium (see below).

What it does
Zinc is essential for the effective absorption of vitamin A, protein synthesis – zinc-containing enzymes help join together the long strings of amino-acids making up each molecule of protein – and cell growth. In the twelve years since its importance was recognised, zinc has been shown to affect profoundly our resistance to infections. Some researchers believe that the increasing vulnerability to disease present in normal aging is due to a declining ability to absorb zinc. The mineral is also essential to the proper functioning of thymic hormones (see pp. 81–84) and so plays a key role in combating infections.

Deficiencies, which are widespread, can be due to faulty diet (see below) but food-refining and processing, pollutants such as the cadmium in car exhausts, and various antagonistic drugs – including the birth control pill – all deplete the body's store.

The most common signs of zinc deficiency are brittle nails, or white spots or lines under the nails. Zinc levels are at their lowest in the week prior to menstruation and a zinc supplement (taken together with B6) can often help reduce pre-menstrual tension.

A lack of zinc also impairs the sense of taste and smell by altering saliva chemistry. Both are, of course, common symptoms of the aging disease. It is also harmful to the health of gums and teeth. Though it is plaque that actually causes gum disease, a zinc deficiency makes the tissues much less capable of resisting the bacterial attack which loosens the teeth and inflames the gums.

Zinc and the food you eat
Recent American research has indicated that the diet of most middle-class adults provides only three-quarters of their RDA, with women obtaining less than men.

Rich natural sources of zinc are fish, especially herrings and oysters (approximately 150mg per 100 grams), and meat (100 grams of lean beef contains around 6mg). Grains, peas, eggs and yeast contain lesser amounts and in a form which is not so easy for the body to absorb. Vegetarians on low-calorie diets are at special risk.

Calcium
FAR recommended range 800–1,000mg per day.

Toxic level: provided it is taken as part of a complete supplement, calcium is non-toxic up to 15,000mg per day.

What it does
The most commonly found mineral in the body, the majority is present in bones and teeth with just 5 per cent serving the nervous system and heart muscles, as well as enzyme reactions. It is needed for the effective employment of vitamin D by the body.

The widespread condition of osteoporosis in post-menopausal women has now been shown to result largely from a low calcium intake. Its uptake by the body can be affected by a high protein diet and excessive zinc supplement as explained above. Absorption is also adversely affected by substances called oxalates found in rhubarb, almonds, chocolate, spinach and beetroot. These should not, therefore, be eaten in excess.

Since a lack of calcium leads to cramps and a general feeling of irritability, milk drinks can help sooth jangled nerves. Hence their value, and popularity, as bedtime drinks.

Calcium and the food you eat
Milk, cheese and sesame seeds are all good sources. A pint of milk contains about 600mg, although pasteurisation is reported to render it less absorbable. A quarter of a pound of sesame seeds contains over 1,000mg. Dolomite is an excellent form of calcium as it also provides magnesium in the correct ratio. Avoid bonemeal, due to the lead content, calcium chloride and calcium lactate. Neither the chloride nor the lactate are necessary and there is less calcium in both than in calcium gluconate. Exercise is

important in maintaining calcium in the bones (see Chapter Ten).

Selenium
RDA: 50–200mcg.
FAR recommended supplement: 250mcg per day.

What it does
During the 1970s it was discovered that cancer rates are lowest in areas where the soil is rich in selenium. Since then this trace element has been promoted from a potential friend to a firm ally in the fight against aging.

Along with vitamins C and E, it is a potent anti-cross-linking agent which also stimulates the immune system and so helps fight infection. Studies among elderly patients in a Finnish retirement home showed that after twelve months on vitamin E and selenium supplements the inmates were less anxious, more alert and better able to look after themselves.

In combination with vitamin E it maintains the health of tissues by promoting capillary fitness. The vitamin removes the toxic by-products of fats from damaging the fragile capillary walls, while selenium acts as a second defensive line by destroying these toxins in the blood.

Selenium and the food you eat
Wheatgerm, fish and organ meats are good sources. In supplements take only organically bound selenium, and steer clear of sodium selenite or selenium dioxide which are less bioavailable and more toxic.

Other minerals essential to health and the effective uptake of vitamins include magnesium, phosphorus, potassium, manganese and iron. These can be obtained in sufficient quantities by adopting the diet procedures described in Chapter Nine. There are two further supplements, choline and lecithin, which I have discussed in Chapter Seven.

Identifying the FAR vitamin plan that's best for you
To determine what level of supplements are needed to

facilitate active regeneration in your own case, use the results from Assessments One and Two. It may well be that you scored high on one assessment and low on the other, or maybe your score was in the low range on both.

The table below allows you to use these two sets of results to pinpoint the supplement plan best suited to your present needs. Along the top you will find the score range for biological aging, down the left side the score range for psychological aging. Locate your own results on each of these, and this will pinpoint the correct plan.

For example, a low score on both means that Plan 1 is appropriate, while a high score on each identifies Plan 9 as being most suitable.

Table 6

		RESULTS ON ASSESSMENT ONE		
		LOW	MEDIUM	HIGH
RESULTS ON	LOW	PLAN 1	PLAN 2	PLAN 3
ASSESSMENT	MEDIUM	PLAN 4	PLAN 5	PLAN 6
TWO	HIGH	PLAN 7	PLAN 8	PLAN 9

(A low score is 10–39 points, a medium score is 40–79 points, and a high score is 80–100 points.)

Note: Whichever plan you follow it is important to take one multi-vitamin tablet per day in addition, in order to maintain a balanced intake (use a high-potency mega-strength variety wherever possible). You must also adopt the diet procedures described in the next chapter. Remember that vitamin supplements must work in conjunction with sound nutrition. They are *not a substitute for food*. (* Indicates that the required B vitamins can be obtained by taking a mega B complex.)

Plan 1
Vitamins: A: 10,000 IUs; B1: 75mg; B2: 75mg; B3: 75mg;
B5: 75mg; B6: 75mg; B12: 10mcg*; C: 1 gram; E: 500 IUs;
folic acid: 400mcg.
Minerals: zinc: 4mg; calcium: 800mg; selenium: 250mg.
PLUS: one multi-vitamin tablet.

Plan 2
Vitamins: A: 10,000 IUs; B1: 75mg; B2: 75mg; B3: 75mg;
B5: 75mg;☆ B6: 100mg; B12: 10mcg*; C: 1 gram; E: 500
IUs; folic acid: 400mcg.
Minerals: zinc: 4mg; calcium: 800mg; selenium: 250mg.
PLUS: one multi-vitamin tablet.

Plan 3
Vitamins: A: 10,000 IUs; B1: 75mg; B2: 75mg; B3: 75mg;
B5: 75mg*; B6: 100mg; B12: 50mcg; C: 1 gram; E: 100
IUs; folic acid: 400mcg.
Minerals: zinc: 4mg; calcium: 800mg; selenium: 250mg.
PLUS: one multi-vitamin tablet.

Plan 4
Vitamins: A: 10,000 IUs; B1: 250mg; B2: 100mg; B3:
100mg; B5: 500mg; B6: 100mg; B12: 50mcg; C: 1 gram; E:
500 IUs; folic acid: 400mcg.
Minerals: zinc: 5mg; calcium: 1000mg; selenium: 250mg.
PLUS: one multi-vitamin tablet.

Plan 5
Vitamins: A: 15,000 IUs; B1:250mg; B2: 100mg; B3:
100mg; B5: 500mg; B6: 100mg; B12: 50mcg; C: 2 grams;
D: 400 IUs; E: 1,000 IUs; folic acid: 400mcg.
Minerals: zinc: 5mg; calcium: 1,000mg; selenium: 250mg.
PLUS: one multi-vitamin tablet.

Plan 6
Vitamins: A: 20,000 IUs; B1: 500mg; B2: 200mg; B3: 400mg; B5: 500mg; B6: 200mg; B12: 50mcg; C: 3 grams; D: 400 IUs; E: 1,000 IUs; folic acid: 600mcg.
Minerals: zinc: 5mg; calcium: 1,000mg; selenium: 250mg.
PLUS: one multi-vitamin tablet.

Plan 7
Vitamins: A: 20,000 IUs; B1: 500mg; B2: 200mg; B3: 400mg; B5: 500mg; B6: 200mg; B12: 50mcg; C: 3 grams; D: 600 IUs; E: 500 IUs; folic acid: 600mcg.
Minerals: zinc: 5mg; calcium: 1,000mg; selenium: 250mg.
PLUSS: one multi-vitamin tablet.

Plan 8
Vitamins: A: 20,000 IUs; B1: 500mg; B2: 300mg; B3: 500mg; B5: 500mg; B6: 300mg; B12: 100mcg; C: 5 grams; D: 600 IUs; E: 1,000 IUs; folic acid: 600mcg.
Minerals: zinc: 5mg; calcium: 1,000mg; selenium: 250mg.
PLUS: one multi-vitamin tablet.

Plan 9
Vitamins: A: 20,000 IUs; B1: 500mg; B2: 300mg; B3: 500mg; B5: 500mg; B6: 400mg; B12: 100mcg; C: 6 gram; D: 600 IUs; E: 1,000 IUs; folic acid: 600mcg.
Minerals: zinc: 5mg; calcium: 1,000mg; selenium: 250mg.
PLUS: one multi-vitamin tablet.

Nine: Eating your way to health

'He may live without books, what is knowledge
but grieving?
He may live without hope, what is hope but
deceiving?
He may live without love, what is passion but
pining?
But where is the man that can live without
dining?'

(Owen Meredith, *Lucile*)

How do you feel about food? Is eating something you look
forward to, think about and take trouble over? Or do you see
it as just another tedious domestic chore to get done with as
rapidly as possible? Whether you are a gourmet or a glutton,
a fastidious diner or a fast-food fan, you'll certainly have an
opinion about eating.

Although there is no need to be fanatical about your food,
refusing anything except organically grown vegetables and
never allowing a sugary dessert to pass your lips, an intelligent attitude towards food is essential for healthy
longevity. While this does not mean that you must worry
excessively about every mouthful at every meal, it does require you to understand the basic facts of nutrition and
approach eating in an intelligent way. Your head should
control your stomach rather than the other way around.

As the eminent nutritionist Adele Green pointed out more
than a decade ago – *we are what we eat.*

Since that time, hundreds of reports and surveys have
confirmed the central role of diet in safeguarding our
system against the aging disease. For example, a recent
study by Professor Givi Abdushelishvili, of the Institute of
Nutrition of Soviet Georgia, has shown that eating habits
are one of the main reasons why that state has one of the
world's highest proportion of healthy centenarians in the
population. He concluded that long-lived people 'are moderate eaters and the calorie values of their diets are lower

than those usually recommended by doctors. They eat chiefly vegetable foods with low cholesterol.'

This doesn't mean that I shall be advising you in this chapter to abandon meat and embrace muesli, however. It may well be that you'll have to make some changes in your eating habits, but it's my belief that these should be introduced slowly and be as minimal as possible — not because a radical change might not be extremely beneficial, but simply because most people find it almost impossible to change the eating habits of a lifetime overnight. To paraphrase a comment originally applied to politics, 'healthy eating is the art of the possible'.

In the long term no diet plan is of the slightest help unless it results in a revision of basic eating patterns. And before embarking on such a quest, bear in mind that you've spent a lifetime developing your present approach to food. Any change must take time.

In some cases it may require years for the switch to new, but no less enjoyable, dietary patterns to take place. So be patient with yourself when tackling this aspect of the FAR programme. Accept, before you even begin, that there are going to be lapses, occasions when you slide back into your previous, unhealthy habits.

For the same reason, the FAR diet procedures do not include endless tables giving you the number of calories and amounts of fat, protein, carbohydrate, minerals and vitamins in every conceivable kind of food. While these are occasionally helpful (I have listed books which provide such information in the bibliography), I have always doubted whether most people have either the interest or the time to plan their diets meticulously according to such precise schedules. Would you be willing to calculate, to the last kilocalorie, how much you'll be eating today? I suspect very few do so occasionally, and only an extremely small number on a regular basis. I believe it is much more important to provide the outlines of a programme which will enhance health and longevity, rather than to try and dictate your diet.

By understanding something about the values of foods and what they can do for you, it is possible to eat with your whole body in mind, rather than being seduced by your eyes, tongue and taste.

The FAR diet plan consists of the twenty-one key points which are listed below. There are *seven* things to avoid, *seven* to adopt and *seven* ways of making your food and vitamins work most efficiently.

The FAR food programme

Over the next few weeks or months you should make a real effort to: *decrease* your intake of:

1 refined sugar
2 salt
3 fatty foods, meat, cream, milk, cheese, butter
4 tea and coffee
5 high-calorie foods
6 alcohol
7 convenience foods

At the same time *increase* your intake of:

1 fibre
2 fish
3 fresh fruit
4 raw vegetables
5 organically grown foods
6 variety in your diet
7 water

While doing this, enhance your absorption of all nutrients by:

1 eating in small amounts
2 avoiding distractions
3 satisfying hunger not habit
4 taking fat-soluble vitamins correctly
5 taking calcium correctly
6 taking vitamins correctly
7 taking iron correctly

As you'll agree, these are not difficult guidelines to follow but if diligently applied they are going to help transform your health, safeguard your heart and prolong your life. Let's consider each in more detail to see why it has so important a role to play in Facilitated Active Regeneration.

One – The perils of hidden sugar

Even if you don't have a sweet tooth and never add sugar to your tea or coffee, it is likely that you are still eating more than half your own weight, or in excess of 100lbs, of sugar each year. About a quarter of a pound per day.

This includes not only 'processed' or 'commercial' sugar, the kind described by Professor John Yudkin, Emeritus Professor of Nutrition at London University, as 'pure, white and deadly'. A telling, if not entirely accurate, phrase since brown sugar is just as unhealthy as white!

During the past two centuries there has been a twenty-five-fold rise in sugar production and consumption, the greatest increase being between 1938 and 1958 when output more than doubled. By comparison, meat and grain consumption rose by only 50 per cent, and milk by 30 per cent. Over the last fifteen years, as more and more people became aware of the hazards of white sugar, there has been a slow but sustained decline in sales of packaged sugar. Yet, at the same time, these same people have actually *increased* their consumption of sugar without even realising it, as manufacturers add more and more to processed foods. A decade ago about half the sugar we ate came from packages. Today two-thirds – a staggering 2,500,000 tons a year – is hidden in other food products.

The dozen popular foodstuffs listed below reveal where some of this vast quantity goes.

Foodstuff	Approximate sugar content (grams)
Chocolate digestive biscuit	9
Shortcake biscuit	2
Slice sponge cake	7
Doughnut	11
Slice chocolate cake	9

Foodstuff	Approximate sugar content (grams)
Small chocolate bar	17
Packet instant custard	34
Small carton fruit yoghurt	22
Portion apple crumble	23
Pint of beer	13
Can of Coca-Cola	35
Small tin of fruit	26

In addition, sugar turns up in many products where you might not expect it. Muesli may have a healthy image, but it also contains 25 per cent sugar; four tablespoons will add nearly 16 grams to your daily consumption. Unless the label specifically states otherwise, it is a fair bet that all tinned food contains added sugar. A small tin of baked beans, for example, contains 10 grams, and similar-sized tins of sweetcorn or kidney beans 7 grams. Even three teaspoons of coffee essence will give you 5 grams of hidden sugar.

Sugar poses a health problem for two main reasons. First, because it supplies calories but no nourishment. For this reason they are often called 'empty calories'. So it can satisfy your energy needs while actually starving your body of the essential raw materials needed for healthy growth.

The second hazard arises because most people eat far too much of it. Mainly because, as we have seen, it is concealed in other foods, which are often not regarded as having a high sugar content. And the major source of this sugar is sucrose, obtained from sugar cane or sugar beet.

Sucrose is termed a disaccharide because when digested it breaks down to form two other kinds of sugars – glucose and fructose; 100 grams of sucrose yields equal amounts of glucose and fructose. For most of human history our systems have been used to handling small amounts of sugar, in the form of fructose obtained from the fruits and honey which have always been part of our diet. Until two centuries ago, only about 8 grams of fructose were consumed per person per day.

Today, as we have seen, some 4 ounces or around 114

grams of sucrose, the equivalent of 56 grams of fructose, are consumed daily. To this must be added the fructose obtained from fruit, bringing the average amount to some 75 grams daily. A quantity almost ten times greater than our digestion was intended by nature to handle. The consequences to our health are severe.

The glucose released when sucrose is broken down in the body poses no problem since the cells rapidly convert it into energy. Fructose, however, metabolises to produce acetate, a precursor of cholesterol. The more sugar you eat the higher your blood cholesterol levels and the greater your risk of coronary heart disease.

In an early study of this link, John Yudkin compared the rate of coronary heart disease with sugar intake across fifteen countries. He found that the death rate per 100,000 people increased steadily from 60 for each 20lbs of sugar consumed per head to 300 for 120lbs and 750 for 150lbs.

The conclusion is clear and unavoidable. Degeneration can be significantly inhibited by cutting down the amount of sugar you eat each day.

What to do
Stop taking sugar with your tea and coffee. Each heaped teaspoon contains about 9 grams of sucrose. If you can't do this immediately, then gradually reduce the amount taken. Don't eat breakfast cereals with added sugar; even a modest serving will contain around 30 grams. Eat fresh fruit rather than pastries, sweets or other desserts with a high sugar content. Limit your consumption of soft drinks to no more than three a week. If you can cut them out entirely then do so. Switch to club soda, which is simply carbonated water. Read the contents labels on cans with care. Remember that 'sucrose', 'dextrose', 'maltose', 'raw sugar', demerera sugar', 'glucose syrup' and 'molasses' are all sugars.

Retrain your taste buds to appreciate lower levels of sweetness. If you can reduce your present intake, which is probably very close to the average 120lbs per year, by half you will be fifteen times less likely to die of coronary heart disease and your risk of contracting adult-onset diabetes will also be significantly reduced.

Two – The problem with salt

We each consume about three heaped teaspoons, or around 10 grams of salt (sodium chloride) a day, even though our body needs less than one-tenth of a teaspoon, little more than 200mg, of sodium daily for good health.

For certain 'salt-resistant' individuals this poses few problems. They can take up to 15 grams daily without showing any adverse reactions. Others, and this may include up to half the adult population, are far more susceptible to its ill- effects. If your family has a history of high blood pressure then the chances are that you are in this latter group.

A high salt consumption is hazardous because the sodium it contains increases your blood pressure, which makes it especially dangerous for hypertensives and not that much safer for those with normal blood pressure. We can all benefit greatly by drastically limiting our consumption.

The list below shows where most people get their salt.

Source	Percentage
Cereals and bread	33
Meat and meat products	17
Other foods	17
Salt added at the table or in cooking	33

What to do

Don't eat too much of the following: cheeses, tinned vegetables, instant meals in pots, crisps, biscuits, salted nuts, bacon, ham, salami, sausages, fish fingers, burgers, stock cubes, meat and yeast extracts, packet soups, breakfast cereals (most have a fairly high sodium content, check the package), smoked and tinned fish.

Foodstuffs which have less than 200mg of sodium per 100 grams of food include: herbs, spices, garlic, vinegar, lemon juice, lean fresh meat, fresh and frozen vegetables, nuts, raisins and raw fruit, unsalted butter and margarine. Among breakfast cereals low in sodium are oats, muesli, Puffed and Shredded Wheat.

Switch from regular salt to light salt (which consists of only half sodium chloride and half potassium chloride) and try to substitute other flavourings such as wine, herbs, spices or lemon. Eat less processed food and increase your consumption of foods high in potassium (see below).

Reduce your intake of salt slowly. If you take a lot of exercise and sweat a great deal you'll need to consume more than a sedentary person. A sign that your salt level has fallen too low too rapidly is muscle cramp, especially in the calf. But the cause could also be dehydration, so drink more water (not coffee or tea).

If it persists, or returns, then maintain a constant salt intake for a few days and the problem should disappear. If it remains, however, increase salt consumption slightly, stay at this new level for a fortnight, and then start cutting down again.

Three – Fitter not fatter

A century ago, fat made up less than a quarter of the average diet. Today we obtain nearly half our energy from fats in different forms. The list below shows the contribution made by different foodstuffs to this total in a typical diet.

Source	Percentage
Meat products	26
Margarine	13
Cooking fats	12
Milk	12
Butter	11
Cheese and cream	7
Biscuits, cakes and pastry	6
Eggs	3
Other	10

The link between the high levels of cholesterol created by such a diet and heart disease were discussed in Chapter Three. But it should be emphasised that it is not only those in the upper 10 per cent who are at risk.

Many of the middle-aged American males who will die

prematurely from a coronary in the next twelve months have cholesterol levels which are only moderately elevated. In a study of 356,222 men aged between thirty-five and fifty-seven, Dr Jeremiah Stamler of Northwestern University Medical School found that increased risk of mortality started at cholesterol levels just above 180mg per decilitre of blood – a level which many doctors, and even cardiologists, would regard as perfectly safe.

The work of Dr Stamler and his colleagues showed that the relationship between cholesterol levels and mortality could be represented by a graded curve. When the cholesterol levels were between 182 and 202 over a six-year period, the death rate among men who developed coronary heart disease was 29 per cent. At between 203 and 220 the death rate rose by 73 per cent; levels of 221–245 raised it by 121 per cent, while above this value the risk rose by 242 per cent. This danger existed even for non-smokers with normal blood pressure.

However, the good news to emerge from the study was that cutting back on fats and high cholesterol foods considerably reduces the risk of heart attacks.

What to do
Foods which you should eat only in moderation include: anything cooked with fat (including gravy from meat fat); tinned meat, sausages, burgers, pasties, salami and meat pies (these are also high in salt); full-fat cheeses, such as Cheddar, Cheshire and blue cheeses; milk, whole or evaporated, and all types of cream including ice-cream; mayonnaise and salad cream; roast and chipped potatoes; biscuits, cakes, pastries; chocolates, toffees, savoury snacks, crisps.

I am not saying that none of these should ever be eaten. But keep them as a minor part of your overall diet. For preference select from the following foods, all of which are low in fat: grilled, baked, poached, boiled, steamed or casseroled food; dried beans, lentils, baked beans, split peas; fish, skinned turkey or chicken, lean meat, rabbit, offal; skimmed or semi-skimmed milk; buttermilk and low-fat yoghurt; bread, crispbreads, muffins, fruit breads; nuts, dried raw fruit; raw vegetables; boiled, baked and mashed potatoes. Change from butter or hard margarine (made from hydrogenated oil), to soft margarine which is produced from unhydrogenated oil. Eat no more than four egg yolks per week. Replace hard fats with cold-pressed oils, olive and sunflower. Trim all visible fat off meat before eating and discard the skin of fowl.

Reducing your fat intake could mean that you will start feeling a bit hungry, so replace the fat with bulkier foods like potatoes and other vegetables. The metabolism of animal fats requires a great deal of energy, so by cutting back you should start feeling more vital and vigorous. But don't attempt to cut out fats completely as they are essential to health.

Four – The caffeine trap

Some of my clients drink ten or more cups of strong tea or coffee a day, and then wonder why they have jangled nerves. When drunk in moderation, up to three cups a day, tea and coffee should pose no problems. Beyond that you could be suffering a variety of unpleasant physical and emotional consequences.

Caffeine, which is present in cocoa, chocolate and cola, as well as coffee and tea, is a potent stimulant which affects the heart, kidneys, lungs and arteries, as well as the whole of the central nervous system. It is believed to act by inhibiting the enzyme which normally breaks down the energy-producing chemical called cyclic adenosine monophosphate (AMP). The resulting increase in cyclic AMP stimulates the production of glucose within the cells, thus making available more energy and enabling the cells to be more active. The caffeine content of various beverages and food is shown below:

	Caffeine in mg per cup
Coffee:	
Percolated	110–65
Instant	90–135
Decaffeinated	2–5

	Caffeine in mg per cup
Tea (Indian) brewed for:	
One minute	*10–35*
Three minutes	*20–40*
Five minutes	*25–60*
Cocoa	*3–10*
Chocolate (1oz): Milk	*1–15*
Cooking	*25–30*
Cola (per bottle)	*35–45*

The brain is stimulated by doses as low as 100mg to become more alert and wakeful, and thoughts flow more swiftly. The heart pumps blood faster, while dilation of the coronary arteries improves its own blood flow. The vessels serving the brain are constricted, reducing blood flow and so bringing relief from headaches caused by hypertension. In moderation, therefore, caffeine brings about agreeable psychological and physiological effects.

When too much is consumed, however, it produces such symptoms as insomnia, restlessness, anxiety and depression. The heart may beat irregularly and, at high doses, mild delirium can even be induced. As with all stimulants, there is a rebound once the effects have worn off. Clear-thinking may be replaced by lethargy and gloom, alertness by deep fatigue and a marked decline in performance.

A study by Annette Rossignol of Tufts University Massachusetts has also shown a link between caffeine consumption and pre-menstrual tension. Of women who drank between 4.5 and 15 caffeine-rich drinks each day, 61 per cent reported moderate to severe symptoms, compared with only 16 per cent of non-caffeine drinkers.

What to do
Cut down slowly, especially if you are caught in the caffeine trap. Try various substitutes, including herbal teas and decaffeinated coffee. Don't eat too many chocolate bars – we've seen that they are unhealthy on account of their sugar and fat content as well. Try not to drink more than four caffeine-rich drinks per day, less if you can manage it.

Five – The fuel we need
The average quantity of food energy required by men is
between 2,000 and 3,5000 calories a day; for women the
range is 1,600 to 2,400. Our needs vary according to the
amount of work we are doing and the surrounding temperature. We saw in an earlier chapter how much energy is
devoted to maintaining a steady internal body temperature.

To determine the energy value of foods they are burned
in a sealed container and the amount of heat given off is
meeasured. For every 1100 grams, fat yields 900 kcal,
starch 415 and protein about 430. Sucrose, lactose (milk
sugar) and maatose supply 395 kcal, glucose and fructose
375 kcaal.

Where are we most likely to get these calories from? A
recent survey of 12,000 US adults showed that among the
top ten contributors of calories were: white bread, rolls and
crackers (9.6 per cent); doughnuts, cookies andd cakes (5.7
per cent); alcohol (5.6 per cent); milk (4.7 per cent),
hamburgers, cheeseburgers and meatloaf (4.4 per cent). A
similar eating pattern is also found throughout Europe.

The average Wesmterner obtains 46 per cent of his, or
her, calories from carbohydrates (starch 20 per cent,
sucrose 20 per cent, naturally occurring sugars 6 per cent),
42 per cent from fats and 12 per cent from protein. A
healthier distribution, and one towards which you should
strive, is to reduce fat to 40 per cent and protein to 10 per
cent of the total, while increasing your consumption of
carbohydrate so that it supplies the remaining half of your
energy requirements. Within this 50 per cent, starch
should provide 30 per cent while sucrose and naturally
occurring sugars provided 10 per cent each.

Nutritionists agree that in the affluent West – and
especially the USA – we eat, on average, two or three times
more protein than is needed for renewing the cells. One effect
of this is that larger amounts of urea have to be excreted in
the urine, placing a heavier burden on the kidneys. Dr
Myron Winick of the Institute of Human Nutrition, Columbia
University School of Medicine, recommends a daily protein
intake of 56 and 46 grams respectively for men and women.

What to do

Cut down on meat. Over-consumption of this protein source can produce deficiencies of vitamins B6 and niacin, as well as calcium, iron, zinc, magnesium and phosphorus. During digestion, excess meat in the diet leads to a build-up of toxins, increasing the damage done by free radicals and cross-linking. Have several meatless days each week and try to eat in proportion to the amount of physical energy you are using up each day.

Six – Another little drink

Some people derive a large proportion of their calories from alcoholic drinks. Like those provided by sucrose, these are empty calories which offer the body no nourishment. Keep the level of calories derived from alcohol down to 10 per cent of your total each day. This means no more than two pints of beer or spirits, and a maximum of three glasses of wine, daily.

Seven – Inconvenience foods

Manmade, processed foods tend to be lower in nutrients, higher in additives and more likely to have picked up contaminants, such as lead, during their trip from the factory to your dining-table. Many have no nutritional value at all, particularly snacks sold for children, and cannot be either digested or biochemically assimilated. Preservatives, artificial colourings and flavourings (there are more than 3,000 currently in use) may well be health risks. These are usually identified by E numbers on the packets, and you should inform yourself about the nature of these additives. The book *E For Additives* by Maurice Hanssen and Jill Marsden (published by Thorsons) is an excellent reference.

Now for the seven things to *increase* in your diet.

One – Fibre

A decade ago fibre was considered a 'crank' food. Today its central importance in preventing a wide range of diseases and limiting age-related degeneration is well established and fresh discoveries are being made all the time.

Wheatbran, long known for promoting a healthy digestion, has recently been shown to assist in the metabolism of fat and sugar. Researchers at the University of Surrey supplemented the diets of volunteers with wheatbran and then examined levels of cholesterol in their blood. After just six weeks of eating between 7 and 12 grams (two to three tablespoons) of unprocessed wheatbran as part of their normal daily diet (the exact amount varied according to their weight) the volunteers' HDL cholesterol levels (the beneficial variety) had risen by 46 per cent while levels of harmful LDL cholesterol had fallen by 25 per cent. The extra bran, sprinkled on soups and desserts, raised their dietary fibre intake by 35 per cent.

Fibre comes from plant foods such as seeds, pulses, whole grains, beans, fresh raw fruits and vegetables. It consists of those portions of the foodstuff, known as polysaccharides, which are incapable of being digested by the human body and so pass through virtually intact. By doing so fibre flushes the system clear of cancer-causing and degeneration-promoting toxins.

What to do
Gradually switch from processed cereals to those which are whole grain or lightly milled. Include brown rice, rye, maize flours and rolled oats in your diet. Add bran, from one to three tablespoons depending on your weight, to the food each day.

Two – Fish
As we have already seen, saturated fats are very much the enemies of healthy living, being implicated in such assaults on the system as heart disease, breast cancer, psoriasis, rheumatoid arthritis and migraine headaches.

But there is a paradox. The Greenland Eskimos eat little fibre, few carbohydrates, hardly any vitamins C or E and their diet, which contains more fish than any country in the world, is rich in cholesterol and protein. Conventional wisdom suggests that they should be dropping like flies. In fact they are among the healthiest race on earth. An Eskimo rarely suffers from heart disease, hypertension is uncommon, obesity and rheumatoid arthritis rare, diabetes unknown and they have very low blood cholesterol levels.

For a quarter of a century their health has presented researchers with a baffling problem. Now the mystery has been solved. Fish is rich in a group of unsaturated fatty acids called omega-3, and it is these, scientists now know, which safeguard the heart, keeping arteries clear of blood clots, while reducing harmful cholesterol and triglycerides. The Japanese, whose consumption of fish is six times that of the West, have a substantially lower incidence of heart disease.

But omega-3 does more than protect against heart disease, it also plays an important role in:

- Relieving swelling and pain in arthritis
- Lowering blood pressure
- Curing psoriasis and eczema
- Aiding brain development
- Preventing breast cancer
- Overcoming migraines

Even though the cancer studies are, so far, confined to the laboratory and not every migraine sufferer will be helped by omega 3, it is still easy to see why its discovery has been hailed as the nutritional breakthrough of the decade. What is more, omega-3 can be obtained easily and cheaply from fish. The highest levels are found in Norwegian sardines (5.1 grams per 100-gram serving) and the lowest in haddock (0.16 grams per 100-gram serving).

But omega-3 is not the only reason for adding a lot more fish to your diet. They are an excellent, low-calorie source of protein. A 100-gram (3.5 oz) portion of cooked white fish can give you a third of your daily requirements at a cost of less than 100 calories. Fish livers are rich in vitamins A and D, and the flesh in B vitamins, particularly B6 and niacin. Fish will also give you potassium, iodine, selenium, iron and phosphorus. Prawns, scallops and unboned fish, like sardines, provide the body with calcium while the fluoride they supply could help protect your teeth against dental caries. Shellfish supply zinc.

But there is yet another bonus. Fish are one of the richest sources of nucleic acid, and by increasing their consumption you safeguard the cell's DNA (deoxyribonucleic acid) and RNA (ribonucleic acid), the blueprints regulating every aspect of your body's functioning.

What to do
Among fresh seafoods, sardines score highest on both omega-3 and nucleic acids. Other good sources of both are salmon (3 grams omega-3 per 100-grams serving), mackerel (2.18 grams omega-3 per 100-gram serving) and herring (1.09 grams omega-3 per 100-gram serving). Fish with a low omega-3 rating include haddock, flounder and bass.

You should eat fish at least four times a week, and preferably six. Include sardines on a minimum of two occasions. Avoid kippers, whose (quite unnecessary) colouring is produced by an additive called FK. At the time of writing this synthetic azo dye had not been given an E number and laboratory research has suggested the possibility of adverse effects from two of the colour's constituents.

Because, sadly, shallow waters are now so seriously polluted by the heavy metals from industrial wastes, it is safer to eat only fish which have been trawled from deep waters or commercially farmed, or which come from clean mountain streams. Shellfish from polluted waters can contain toxins, in addition to organisms responsible for hepatitis, cholera and gastro-enteritis.

Buy fish as fresh as possible, keep chilled to safeguard against bacterial growth and eat as soon as possible.

Three and Four – Fresh fruit and vegetables
In the working-class areas of Naples coronary heart disease is rare, cholesterol levels are low and obesity seldom a problem. Poverty protects the people by placing the sugar-rich desserts so popular with wealthier Italians beyond their purse for everyday consumption. As a result

they eat a great deal of fresh fruit, and this prevents them from contracting a wide range of diseases including, very probably, cancer.

In an eleven-year study of more than a million Japanese males, conducted by the American Cancer Society, strong evidence was found that fresh fruit, and fresh fruit juice, offered smokers a degree of protection against lung cancer. Those who ate fresh fruits six or seven times each week were least likely to develop the disease. Smokers who had fruit three or four times a week ran a 25 per cent greater risk, while those who either ate no fruit at all, or only occasionally, were 75 per cent more likely to succumb. Fresh fruit, eaten every day of the week, is an important element in the FAR diet programme. Because it is low in sodium, fruit can be eaten by people with high blood pressure. A glass of milk, for example, contains 126mg of sodium, a large peach under 1mg. Fruit also contains potassium, a mineral which helps reduce blood pressure. Vegetarians usually have low blood pressure, even if their family has a history of hypertension.

Fresh fruit contains pectin, a fibre which protects against heart disease, probably by removing cholesterol from the digestive system before it can be absorbed. It may also protect against gall-stones and colon cancer by flushing bile acids from the intestines. Pectin also chelates (binds) harmful heavy metals, such as aluminium, and so prevents needless degeneration through cross-linking. Heavy metals are potent cross-linking agents.

The natural sugars in fruit (mainly fructose) provide energy without the hazard of a rapid rise in blood sugar levels which result from eating sucrose-rich foods. Here again pectin plays a role, helping to produce a gel-like substance which coats the intestines and slows the uptake of glucose. The same gel slows the passage of food through the system, preventing over-eating due to hunger pangs.

Fruit is low in calories but rich in a whole range of nutrients, including folacin, a B vitamin required for the healthy development of red blood cells and magnesium, in addition to vitamin C and B6.

Vegetables too are an excellent source of fibre and

provide high levels of nourishment at a low cost in calories. Asparagus, mushrooms, beets, cauliflower, spinach and turnip greens are a good source of nucleic acid, and especially important to vegetarians who are unable to get theirs from fish.

What to do

At least one meal a day must include substantial amounts of grated or chopped raw vegetables. Eat fruit for dessert, and as a between-meal snack if you feel hungry, every day of the week. Apples, grapes, oranges and berries are good sources of pectin and should be eaten regularly.

Legumes and pulses (beans, peas, lentils and so on) are an excellent source of protein and far better for you than high-fat meat or sugar-heavy food. Starchy root vegetables – swedes, potatoes etc. – provide complex carbohydrates.

The ABC of healthy eating

Good digestion depends on achieving the correct acid/alkaline balance in the blood. Blood is naturally slightly alkaline, arterial blood having a pH of 7.4. The pH value is a technical term used by scientists to indicate the degree of acidity or alkalinity in a substance. The pH range is from 0 to 14, with 7 as the neutral mid-point. A pH below 7 indicates increasing acidity; the stomach, for instance, has a pH of 0.8 owing to the presence of strong hydrochloric acid. Because the body produces more acid than alkaline substances each day, and must dispose of the excess, normal urine has a pH of 6 as opposed to the 7.4 of arterial blood.

If the blood pH drops below 7.4 the individual is said to be suffering from acidosis; if it rises above this figure he or she, has alkalosis. The fact that nobody can live for more than a few hours with a blood pH below 7.0 or above 7.7 indicates the critical nature of this balance. Fortunately, the body maintains the correct pH very accurately when in a healthy state. Breathing deeply makes us feel livelier and more alert because it alkalises the blood by expelling more carbon dioxide.

However, we can, and often do, upset this delicate

balance by eating foods which are high in acid. Typical Western diets can consist of up to 95 per cent acid-forming foods. Breakfasting on coffee with sugar, toast and marmalade, then lunching on red meat and French fries, means that we pump high levels of acid into the system. The result can be feelings of irritation, depression and a generally negative outlook on life. Excess acidity can increase the risk of arthritis and rheumatism.

Increasing alkaline consumption, which means returning to the eating habits of our hunter-gatherer ancestors, increases positive emotions, generates greater optimism and enhances relaxation. The ideal balance is 80 per cent alkaline/20 per cent acid derived from the breakdown products of the food you eat. To achieve this 8 to 2 ratio adjust your current diet, as necessary, by carrying out a daily acid balance check (ABC).

The list below gives the acidity/alkalinity ratings for a wide range of foods. By keeping a note of what you eat in each group you can easily monitor the balance.

Alkaline-forming foods checklist

ABC Rating 4 (very high alkaline-forming foods): spinach, figs (dried), apricots, raisins, currants, prunes, sultanas.
ABC Rating 3 (high alkaline-forming foods): beetroot, potato, rhubarb, avocado, almonds, dates, peaches, chestnuts.
ABC Rating 2 (medium alkaline-forming foods): carrots, celery, peas (dried), lettuce, parsnips, radishes, turnips, watercress, horseradish, tomatoes, cabbage, haricot, figs (green), lemons, blackberries, apricots, banana, blackcurrants, greengages, Cantaloupe melon, cherries, grapes, loganberries, pineapple, orange, grapefruit, nectarine, raspberries, peaches, honeydew melon, tangerines.
ABC Rating 1 (low alkaline-forming foods): lentils, peas (raw), marrow, onions, mushrooms, plums, apples, pears, strawberries, gooseberries, plums, milk (whole or skimmed), honey.

Acid-forming foods checklist

ABC Rating 4 (very high acid-forming foods): crab, lobster,

prawns, chicken liver, calves' liver, Edam cheese, egg yolk, lean lamb's meat.
ABC Rating 3 (high acid-forming foods): kidney, veal, turkey, chicken, beef, coley, trout, plaice, lemon sole, oysters, cod, halibut, haddock, herring, mackerel, salmon, whole eggs, oatmeal, wholemeal flour.
ABC Rating 2 (medium acid-forming foods): butter beans, Stilton cheese, cheddar, walnuts.
ABC Rating 1 (low acid-forming foods): olives, mustard and cress, asparagus, broad beans, egg white, butter, Brazil nuts, honeycomb, sago, tapioca.

As the checklists show, fruit and vegetables are mostly alkaline-producing, in contrast to acid-producing foodstuffs like meat, dairy products and grains. So for every helping of meat, or fish, you eat make sure you take four helpings of vegetables or fruit.

Five – Buy organically grown if possible
While the cost or inconvenience of buying from shops which guarantee that their products are organically grown may make this difficult, it is well worth the extra cost and effort when at all possible. As we have seen, the nutritional value of foods starts declining as soon as they have been gathered. Remember the loss of vitamins reported in the last chapter. The sooner you are able to eat these foodstuffs the more benefit you'll derive. Organically grown food, apart from – usually – offering better guarantees of freshness, is also less likely to be contaminated with pesticides, herbicides or lead.

Six – Variety is important
There is a far higher incidence of food allergy than is generally recognised, and the majority of sufferers are not even aware that they have a problem. They blame irritability, depression or fatigue, the time of year, the weather or the stress of life, when the real answer could lie in the food they are eating. You can lower the risk of unrecognised

allergy problems by eating a wide variety of foods instead of sticking to a few favourites. In allergy tests foods like white bread or sugar often turn out to be the culprits.

Seven – Drink more water

You don't have to be stranded in the middle of a desert to dehydrate. Exertion which makes you sweat more than usual, pregnancy or taking certain medication all increase your need for water. As you get older your natural thirst mechanism may work less efficiently, so you could be drying out and not realise it. Since 60 per cent of our body is water, dehydration is a serious matter. We each require a litre (two pints) of water a day to function efficiently. After proteins, carbohydrates and fats it is our most important nutrient.

An important function is to flush out the toxins and other harmful substances removed through the kidneys by the blood. The more water you drink the more urine you produce and the less work the kidneys have to do – it takes less energy to excrete dilute than concentrated urine.

A high water intake also prevents the formation of crystals in the body fluids. Gout is caused by the accumulation of sodium urate crystals in joints and tendons; kidney stones are usually formed from urates of calcium and magnesium.

The symptoms of dehydration include light-headedness, muscle cramps, weariness, loss of appetite, impatience and irritability.

What to do

Drink at least two litres (four pints) of water every day. Linus Pauling suggests a glass every hour. But don't drink during meals, or for thirty minutes before and one hour after eating, since this dilutes the gastric juices and makes digestion less efficient. If taking a trip by air which lasts longer than one hour, take bottled water with you and drink a pint an hour. The air-conditioning system in aircraft leads to especially rapid dehydration, which is responsible for many of the symptoms of jet-lag experienced by long-haul travellers.

Food and vitamins
In the last chapter I explained that, in order to get the best from your vitamins, they need to be ingested as efficiently as possible in order to achieve maximum absorption and minimum loss. Diet and styles of eating have an important part to play in this process. In addition to the fourteen points above, add these seven pointers to successful eating.

One – Eat in small amounts
Don't swamp your system. Small, nutritious meals are far better for you than binges. When the digestion is obliged to handle large quantities of food at once, it will fail to absorb many important nutrients.

Two – Don't be distracted
Eating while watching TV can play hell with your weight. The body tells the brain when it has had enough food. But if you are not concentrating on your meal, or eat very quickly, these signals may be missed. As a result you over-eat and put on weight.

Three – Eat to satisfy body needs, not habit
Most people either miss breakfast entirely or limit themselves to high carbohydrate foods. As a result their body experiences an insulin flush in order to process all the glucose which floods into the system. By mid-morning blood-glucose levels have fallen to the point where fatigue sets in. This is usually dealt with by taking more carbohydrates, in the form of an eleven o'clock snack, which simply repeats the earlier error.

Lunch is often rushed or skimped, while the last meal of the day is usually the main meal. This pattern of eating, which owes far more to habit than your body's real needs, is very unhealthy. Eating heavily just before you go to bed means that the body must store what it cannot transform into energy, and since you are asleep and fairly inactive this is more likely to happen at night. When you wake up next morning your blood-glucose level is still high, so you have little appetite for breakfast. So the pattern repeats itself, day in and day out.

The old advice that you should breakfast like a king, lunch like a prince and sup like a pauper is very sound. By including protein in your breakfast you'll slow the digestive process and so release energy gradually during the day, thus avoiding mid-morning sag. A small meal last thing at night means that you wake with an appetite.

Eating protein first thing in the morning can also help you keep your weight down. Research has shown that, owing to the influence of the body clock, calories eaten at the start of the day are more likely to be burned up for energy and less likely to be laid down as fat.

If you get hungry during the day, eat fruit, raw vegetables or wholegrain bread rather than junk foods with their high sugar content.

Four – Take fat-soluble vitamins with fat foods

If you take vitamins A, D and E on an empty stomach or with a meal high in carbohydrates but low in fats, they will be absorbed less efficiently. Fat-soluble vitamins need fat in the guts to get into the body. So swallow them with a glass of low-fat milk, or eat them with your main meal of the day.

Five – Take calcium and vitamin D together

Calcium needs vitamin D in order to be absorbed effectively. It also needs an acid environment, so take it with a meal and, preferably, last thing at night. During the day your body can get sufficient calcium from its food. At night, it may have to draw on natural stores – which means your skeleton – to find enough for its needs. Taking a calcium supplement just before you go to bed maintains blood levels throughout the night and safeguards your bones. If you don't eat at night then take the supplement with low-fat milk.

Six – Have your vitamin C several times a day

The FAR programme includes large doses of vitamin C. These are best taken in smaller amounts throughout the day, preferably with food to aid absorption (eating increases blood flow and so distributes all nutrients around the body more efficiently) and prevent side-effects from the acidity. Research has shown that the more you take at one time the less gets through to your cells.

Seven – Take iron with vitamin C

Iron comes in two kinds – heme, which comes from meat, fish, eggs and poultry, and nonheme obtained from plants. We can absorb up to 30 per cent of heme iron, but only around 10 per cent of the nonheme variety. Vitamin C aids the absorption of nonheme iron by converting it to a form which the body uses more readily. Take iron, or multi-minerals containing iron, with your vitamin C.

By adopting this easily followed eating plan you can bring about all the regeneration-enhancing changes needed to enjoy a long and healthy life. But be patient with yourself and don't feel guilt about occasional lapses. It's no fun munching on a nut cutlet while everybody else is enjoying a celebration banquet, and refusing food which your host and hostess have spent hours preparing is both embarrassing and unnecessary.

As I have already mentioned, in the FAR programme your emotional health is no less important than your physical fitness. So don't be a martyr or try and force yourself to do the impossible. Bring about changes slowly, maybe introducing them just one at a time. That way you are far more likely to stay with the plan until it becomes a routine part of your everyday eating habits.

Ten: Walking your way to wellness

'We also should walk in newness of life.'

(Romans 6:4)

Mankind has existed on this planet for around two million years. If that period was compressed into a single year, the Industrial Revolution would begin at around eleven o'clock on the night of 31 December and modern technology arrive on the scene about eight minutes to midnight.

Because, for the greater part of human history, survival has depended on hunting animals and gathering food rather than labouring in factories or behind office desks, the human body evolved as a machine designed for active muscle work, not passive mind work. 'Whatever the changes we have wrought, and wherever our intelligence and imagination may carry us, we are still connected to the reality of that evolution,' comment Arabella Melville and Colin Johnson in their book *The Long Life Heart*. 'And we are as dependent on it as the tallest tree is dependent on its roots remaining in suitable soil.'

There is ample evidence to show that the mental and physical wellness on which healthy longevity depends can only be achieved by satisfying this evolutionary requirement for frequent, vigorous and sustained exercise.

The benefits of exercise
In a major study directed by Professor David Snowdon of Loma Linda University, California a total of 3,933 initally healthy males, aged between thirty and sixty-three, were

divided into an 'active' and 'non-active' group depending on how much exercise they undertook. After following their fortunes for twenty-one years, the researchers reported that *inactive* men were almost three times as likely to die from heart disease as those taking regular exercise. The team also found an interesting link between lack of exercise and excessive meat consumption. They concluded that while it is equally unwise to eat a lot more meat or take very little exercise, doing both together more than doubles the risk of heart disease.

A similar study under the direction of Dr Ralph Paffenbarger of the Stanford University Medical School followed the medical fortunes of 17,000 former Harvard students with ages ranging from thirty-five to seventy-four. The study started in the mid 1960s, when volunteers completed questionnaires about their health and lifestyle. The subjects were then followed up until 1978, during which period 1,413 of them died – 45 per cent from heart disease, 32 per cent from cancer, 13 per cent from other natural causes and the remaining 10 per cent as a result of accident.

It was found that men who burned up at least 2,000 calories per week through exercise suffered death rates a quarter to one third lower than those who expended fewer calories. Although previous research had shown exercise to be beneficial in protecting people against heart problems, Dr Paffenbarger's work was the first to demonstrate that being active offered protection against all diseases.

Exercise safeguards the whole system by reducing blood pressure, by as much as 10 to 20 points, lowering resting heart rate and improving the functioning of both cardiovascular and lymphatic systems. This ensures that oxygen and nutrients are transported to the cells, and toxic waste products removed from the body, via lymphatic drainage with maximum efficiency.

Results from another recent Harvard study, which this time looked at the health and longevity of 5,400 female university graduates, suggest that taking exercise during the late teens and early twenties can reduce the risk of women developing a wide range of cancers.

When Dr Rose Frisch compared the medical histories of

women ranging in age from twenty-one to eighty with their involvement in sports while at college, she found that athletic women were two and a half times less likely to develop cancers of the cervix, uterus, ovaries and vagina, and twice less likely to get breast cancer.

Not that these 'active' women expended a vast amount of time and effort on their sports. The majority simply went to dance classes, did track events, and played tennis, volleyball or basketball for about five hours a week spread over several sessions.

There is no longer the slightest doubt that if you want to live a long and healthy life you must use your body as actively as nature intended. The question is, what form should such exercise take?

Which exercise is best?

At this point I'd like you to consider the following seven questions. Answer as honestly as you can and keep going until you respond with a no, then ignore the rest:

Do you jog, run or do aerobics?
Does each exercise session last twenty minutes or longer?
Do yoou have four or more exercise sessions each week, every week, at least fifty weeks of the year?
Do you exercise strenuously enough to increase your pulse rate and work up a sweat?
Do you really enjoy your sessions?
Do you hope, and expect, to be exercising in the same way next year?
Do you believe you will still be exercising like this in five years' time?

How far down this list did you get before honesty compelled a no answer?

If you reached the last question and still answered yes, there is not much to be gained from reading the rest of this chapter. You are clearly hooked on a form of exercise that, provided you take care not to push yourself too hard, will facilitate active regeneration. But if you answered no at any stage, either because you tried and abandoned any of those activities, or somehow have never got around to starting, there's no need to abandon hope that the wellness exercise can bring must for ever elude you.

The good news is that you can satisfy your body's need for vigorous activity without ever donning a tracksuit, slipping on a ssweat-band or driving yourself into a state of exhaustion. It is not necessary to visit a gym or pound the pavements in search of greater fitness and a longer life. Recent research has clearly demonstrated that you do not have to jog, run or do aerobics to enjoy a healthy longevity. Anybody who wishes can simply walk their way to wellness.

That's all the FAR exercise procedure involves. Old-fashioned, undramatic walking. Briskly to be sure, so that your raised pulse indicates that your heart is working harder, but without ever breaking into even a modest trot. And correctly, so your body moves naturally with muscles and bones working in effortless harmony with your surroundings. But still only walking, as mankind has done for millions of years. Not running, not jogging, not aerobic exercising. In Paffenbarger's study, described above, five hours of walking was as health-promoting as four hours of jogging – and far less exhausting.

If you enjoy jogging or running – don't stop

I am not claiming that jogging, running or aerobics are bad forms of exercise. When carried out correctly they are excellent. Nor am I suggesting that those who enjoy them should renounce them.

Ever since the unfortunate death of fifty-two-year-old American running guru James Fixx, who dropped dead on Friday, 20 July 1984, while jogging down the Vermont State Highway, there has been a backlash against such strenuous forms of exercise. People who jogged or ran continued to do so, but doubts had been raised about the real contribution of exercise to health. In fact the risks involved in all those sports have been exaggerated. 'That people die during exercise should not come as a surprise,' comment Drs David Ashton and Brice Davies in their book

Why Exercise? 'Most males over forty in Western society have some degree of narrowing of their coronary arteries, and a smaller number have a degree of involvment which is likely to place them at increased risk during vigorous exercise.'

They point out that most heart-disease-related deaths do not take place during exercise, but while people are driving their cars, watching television or working behind a desk. And these occur at the rate of 1,000 a day, or about 42 per hour, in the USA.

A Canadian study estimated the risks of middle-aged businessmen dying during unsupervised gym training at 1 per 2,500 gymnasium hours, while an American survey of jogging gave the figure of 1 death per 7,620 joggers, the equivalent of a fatality for every 396,000 hours of jogging. This compares with a risk to rugby players and referees of one death for each 50,000 hours of rugby for players and one per 3,000 rugby hours for referees.

If you have just taken up jogging or running, or are seriously considering doing so – then let me offer the following advice.

- Start slowly. As soon as you feel short of breath stop running and walk.
- Don't be competitive and push yourself needlessly.
- Read books on the subject (see Bibliography) and buy proper equipment – the correct shoes are especially important.
- Run on grass and in the fresh air whenever possible.
- Work out just hard enough to raise your pulse to the Ideal Exercise Rate (see p. 186).
- Don't jog after a heavy meal or after drinking alcohol.
- At the end of a run slow down and allow your body to cool off, never come to an abrupt halt. There is evidence that a sudden surge of adrenalin follows vigorous activity as the body attempts to restore blood pressure to the level reached at the peak of activity. Far from regulating blood pressure, this surge – during which the hormone may soar to ten times its normal level – can bring about fatal pulse irregularities. Slowly winding down from the exercise will prevent this and keep blood pressure steady.

If you hate jogging or running – don't start

My argument is not that people who love jogging and running must stop, rather that anybody who dislikes these forms of exercise need never start. There can be gain without pain.

The FAR exercise procedure, like the FAR diet plan, is based on the commonsense assumption that it is only human to continue doing things which give us pleasure while avoiding anything that brings discomfort and distress. And what matters where wellness is concerned is that you continue to exercise, day in and day out, month in and month out, from now for the rest of your life. To do this you must get immediate enjoyment and constant pleasure, not just the vague hope you are 'doing yourself good'.

If you follow this proposal you will have to walk every day, for at least thirty minutes – more if you wish, but half an hour daily is all that it takes to build health. And that's all there is to it.

Why walking wins

Walking offers many bonuses in addition to building fitness.

- Walking is sociable. Because you never get out of breath, you'll be able to talk as you walk, so that, with the right companion, both mind and body may be stimulated simultaneously.
- Walking is interesting. If you are able to take at least some of your walks in unfamiliar and agreeable surroundings, every turn in the road, the brow of each hill, offers new views and fresh surprises.
- Walking is convenient, easy and cheap. There is no need to dress up in expensive clothes. It can be done anywhere. You can walk in the town and cities just as easily as in open country, although countryside or parks are preferable because the air is cleaner and grass far kinder to legs and feet than concrete.
- Walking is non-competitive. There is no need, or desire, to drive yourself to walk faster than the next person. So there is no temptation to force yourself beyond your physical limits.

- Walking is its own reward – an end in itself, a pleasurable activity – rather than merely what is, for many, the slightly disagreeable means to the goal of greater fitness.

Describing walking as 'the ideal exercise in virtually every respect', cardiologist Dr Henry Solomon comments that 'walking, like swimming, uses the correct large muscles for conditioning; and if you swing your arms freely and naturally, you get additional benefits that way. Your pace is obviously easily varied, and you can adjust it instantly.'

You will find guidelines for getting the most out of walking on the FAR plan below.

The benefits of walking

Research has clearly demonstrated that moderate exercise can be just as health-promoting, and far less health-threatening, as driving yourself to exercise too hard, or too fast. There is absolutely no reason to sweat and suffer in order to build fitness and stamina.

Research by David Mymin at the University of Manitoba in Canada, for example, has shown that the beneficial effects resulting from strenuous exercise, including a decrease in high density lipoprotein (HDL) and blood insulin levels, can be achieved by merely taking a brisk walk. Before this study, it had been assumed that only distance runners and dedicated athletes could achieve an increase in HDL. As we have seen, a high level of HDL helps keep the bloodstream free of clogging cholesterol. This finding was confirmed by doctors at Pennsylvania State University, who found that the moderate exercise provided by a brisk twenty-minute walk significantly raises HDL levels in middle-aged women.

Dr Mymin also showed that walking improves the supply of oxygen to the cells and enhances the elimination of toxic wastes – including cell-corrupting free radicals.

In a study at the University of Wisconsin, brisk walking (at more than four miles per hour) was found to increase heart rate up to 87 per cent of capacity, the same amount attained by cyclists and only 3 per cent less than that achieved by runners.

Even after significant degeneration has occurred, walking often proves extremely beneficial. In a study of men at high risk from coronary heart disease, doctors at the University of Minnesota School of Public Health showed that such exercise was an excellent way of protecting them against attacks.

Walking can also help with emotional problems; it has been shown to lift depression and reduce anxiety. 'Unhappy business men, I am convinced, would increase their happiness more by walking six miles every day than by any conceivable change in philosophy,' wrote the mathematician and philosopher Bertrand Russell.

If your job is mentally taxing, walking will help clear the thoughts and stimulate the flow of ideas. The famous French novelist Gustave Flaubert, author of *Madame Bovary* among other classics, used to take long walks before sitting down to write, and claimed that it enhanced his creativity.

The Greek philosopher Aristotle was so convinced walking and thinking went together that he founded the Peripatetic (walking around) School of Philosophy. Other great thinkers who found walking aided their mental powers were the English romantic poet Wordsworth (who is reported to have walked more than 180,000 miles in his lifetime), Jane Austen, Walt Whitman, Robert Frost, Thomas Jefferson, Robert Louis Stevenson and Ralph Waldo Emerson.

Scientific evidence in support of a link between walking and enhanced mental powers comes from a study by Dr Robert Dustman at the neuropsychology laboratory of the Veterans' Administration Medical Centre in Salt Lake City. He placed a group of sedentary people, aged between fifty-five and seventy, on a sixteen-week walking programme. Each volunteer walked briskly for one hour, on a treadmill to ensure consistent speeds, three times each week. When at the end of training their performance on a range of intelligence tests – which assessed memory, mental agility, response time and visual organisation ability – was compared with non-exercise subjects of equal intelligence, they did significantly better.

In a similar study, which focused on students who

suffered from high levels of anxiety during exams, moderate walking for twenty minutes at a time was better at calming jangled nerves than either meditation training, for the same amount of time, or a pill which purported to be a tranquilliser but was actually an inert placebo.

Walking strengthens your calf muscles, and by doing so eases the strain on your heart through improved efficiency of what is called the muscle pump. One of the toughest jobs the heart has to do is to pump blood all the way up from the feet. It is assisted in this arduous, gravity-defying task by the leg muscles, which 'pump' blood by compressing the veins as they extend and contract. Denied this assistance, the heart may not be able to deliver sufficient blood to the brain. As a result you faint, so bringing the level of the head below that of the heart and restoring flow. Guardsmen obliged to stand at attention for long periods may pass out as a result of the absence of muscle-pump assistance to their heart. Strong leg muscles are essential to a healthy cardiovascular system.

Posture is important
Watching the way most people move around offers an object lesson in poor posture. Many are walking not to wellness but into a doctor's consulting-room or to the osteopath's couch. Observe how often backs are hunched, shoulders droop and stomachs sag. Now and then, however, amongst this dispiriting parade of woefully abused bodies, you'll catch sight of somebody who knows how to move, who seems to glide rather than stride, effortlessly, naturally and gracefully.

Think of your body as a vastly complicated machine, designed to operate efficiently by means of rods (bones) and elastic (muscles and tendons) over a fairly limited range of movements. Outside this range it can still function, after a fashion, but far less effectively and with a significant increase in wear and tear. When used according to nature's intentions, not only is less energy expended in carrying out any activity, but deterioration is reduced to a minimum. Endurance and stamina increase and longevity is enhanced.

Posture is a vital but seldom considered aspect of exercising. After all, any piece of complicated machinery will last much longer if made to work as the designer and manufacturer intended.

Back problems provide a tragic example of what can go wrong as a result of incorrect posture. Millions suffer great discomfort or considerable pain as a result of slipped discs, pulled muscles and strained tendons. It is one of the most frequently encountered problems in medicine.

To see what goes wrong, try snapping a match while holding it upright on a hard surface and applying pressure directly downward. In this position even this fragile stick of wood possesses considerable strength. Now angle the match slightly and repeat the attempt. This time the wood will splinter easily. It is the same with the twenty-four separate vertebrae that make up most of the spine.

While your back remains straight, with all the weight directed downward, the separate vertebrae have a strength equal to, or greater than, any other single bone in the body. But if curved even a little, the same force which was resisted with ease by a vertical back can cause serious problems. The most likely effect is that one of the inter-vertebral fibrocartilage discs, which act as shock absorbers, will slip out of place. When extreme, such slippage causes severe pain through pressure on any of the many nerve fibres which pass up the spinal chord on their way to the brain.

When walking make sure to adopt the following rules of posture. You may find it helpful to practise in front of a mirror.

- Draw in the base of the spine so your back is straight – you'll notice that this tends to flatten the stomach. Keep the muscles in your buttocks taut. This single improvement in posture will do much to reduce the risk of low-back problems.
- Drop and relax your shoulders. This does not mean that you can allow them to droop forward, but nor must they be drawn back in classic parade-ground style.
- Your chin should be held parallel to the floor. Imagine that a string extends from each ear and holds your head upright.

Imagine the strings are being drawn steadily and evenly upwards, so that your head feels almost weightless. Do not allow it to tilt back, as this strains neck and shoulder muscles leading to painful stiffness. Walk with your body held in this manner. Practise until your movements feel natural, harmonious and are completely free from stress or tension. You must never be uncomfortable or unnatural in your movements.

Calculating your walking speed

Simply by walking briskly, so that your pulse is speeded and you feel a pleasant warmth in your muscles, you'll achieve a major leap forward in wellness. But if you aren't worried by some simple arithmetic and would like to add science to your sessions, then a more accurate method for determining how much energy you should expend on walking is to calculate what is termed your Ideal Exercise Rate. This is the level of effort needed to improve physical functioning, without placing you at any risk of overdoing things.

The relationship between effort and reward is illustrated below.

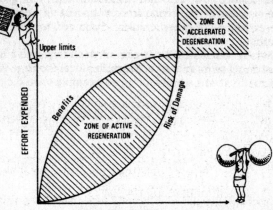

As you can see, up to a certain point the effort expended increases the benefits derived from exercise. This is the zone of active regeneration.

Beyond this upper limit, however, you gain no additional advantages from your continued investment of effort. Indeed, due to the increasing risk of damaging the system, you enter the zone of accelerated degeneration. In his Harvard study, Dr Paffenbarger found that a regimen which burned up 3,500 calories, compared with the 2,000 achieved through moderate exercise, produced no significant benefits while substantially increasing the risk of injuries.

Using your heart rate – measured by taking the pulse at regular intervals – to dictate the effort expended, you can be sure to remain well within the lower, regenerative zone. Carry out the calculation as follows:

Sit down, relax for a few moments and then take your resting pulse. Do this either by placing two fingers at the angle of the jaw and feeling the beat of the carotid pulse or by taking the wrist (radial) pulse. Count the beats for six seconds, then multiply by ten to get the number of beats per minute. Next, subtract your age from 220 to determine the maximum desirable heart rate. The difference between your resting pulse rate and maximum heart rate gives the exercise range (the range from your resting heart rate to the fastest your heart should be allowed to beat during exercise).

Finally, calculate 75 per cent of this range and add it to the resting pulse rate to produce the Ideal Exercise Rate. If the maths seems a bit baffling, an example should clear up any confusions.

Suppose you are forty-four years old and have a resting heart rate of 60 beats per minute. The calculation, which is quick and easy to carry out, is then simply:

Maximum heart rate = $220 - 44 = 176$

Exercise range (maximum heart rate − resting pulse rate) = $176 - 60 = 116$

75 per cent of that range = 87

Ideal Exercise Rate = $60 + 87 = 147$

Now work out your own Ideal Exercise Rate using the guide below:

My resting pulse =

My maximum heart rate (220 minus my age) =

My exercise range is (maximum heart rate − resting pulse rate) =

75 per cent of my exercise range =

Ideal Exercise Rate (resting pulse rate + 75 per cent of exercise range) =

Try and keep your heart beating at this rate for most of the thirty minutes of your walk. When starting, check your pulse every five minutes – it can be done unobtrusively and without stopping. After a short while you will find that you know when your heart is expending the correct amount of effort from the way you feel. If in good shape already you may need to jog a little between periods of walking to raise your pulse by the required amount.

The FAR plan for wellness walking

There are just seven things to remember when you start walking your way to wellness:

1 Walk every day for at least thirty to forty minutes – longer if you like, and have the time.

2 Keep up a brisk pace, between four and five miles per hour.

3 Lengthen your stride when walking briskly, but experiment with different strides until you find one which is comfortable.

4 Take care of your feet. Keep toenails short. Wear shoes which are flat and comfortable. Trainers or good-quality running shoes are fine so long as the ground is dry. If they work loose, stop at once to tighten the laces as this will prevent heel blisters. On long walks turn your sock inside out to avoid chafing the little toe against the seam.

5 Vary your pace, and don't always cover the same ground. Adding variety to your walking programme keeps the mind as stimulated as the body.

6 Try and leave your worries behind you. Concentrate on your surroundings. Problems banished to the back of the mind are still

being worked on by areas of the brain below your level of
awareness. On coming back from a walk you may be surprised to
find the answers which earlier proved so elusive.

7 Take every opportunity of walking. Climb stairs instead of using
the elevator. Never ride when you can walk.

Other ways of exercising

Even if you walk regularly you can enhance your health still
further by enjoying sports. Swimming is excellent. It exercises
all the major muscle groups and, because the body is supported
by the water, avoids the constant shock and jarring which
occur when running on hard surfaces. Cycling too provides
good cardiovascular exercise. I often recommend a rebound
training programme to my clients, which involves bouncing
on a small trampoline. This not only stimulates the heart, but
also improves lymphatic drainage since, for a brief moment at
the climax of a bounce, the body defies gravity. I have found
that anxiety is reduced and depression lifted by regular twelve-
minute sessions on one of these bouncers.

All these forms of exercise work in conjunction with the
FAR eating plan to assist in weight loss. What none of them
will do is strengthen or shape upper body muscles. If you want
to do this, you'll need to do weight-training or isometrics
(these are exercises involving repeated muscle contractions
against a temporary fixed resistance).

One of the major benefits you will get from such workouts is
a better-looking body. Such a goal should not be dismissed as
mere vanity. If you feel confident about your appearance,
your self-esteem increases and you are more likely to tackle
challenges with assurance and vigour. By looking younger
than your chronological age you may also safeguard yourself
against some of the social causes of aging – mainly the attitudes
and opinions of others – which I described in Chapter Two.

There could also be a gain in health through a reduction of
blood pressure. Studies of hypertension in more than 4,000
men, by Carol Buck and Alan Donner at the University of
Western Ontario, showed that those whose work involved
even a moderate level of isometrics, such as pulling levers or

lifting heavy objects, had lower blood pressures than men whose jobs required no such activities.

Build your fitness slowly, especially if you have not exercised for some considerable time and are overweight. Never push yourself to go too far or do too much. If you have a history of heart disease, have just come out of hospital or have difficulties breathing then seek medical advice before embarking on any form of exercise programme.

Making FAR a part of your lifestyle

As you have seen, to enhance your natural powers of regeneration in order to live a long and healthy life, thus enjoying peak performance past forty, you need do little more than common sense suggests. Eat sensibly, take regular – but not necessarily overly strenuous – exercise, avoid hazardous environments and, perhaps most important of all, maintain a positive and hopeful attitude towards life.

Only by achieving such balance and harmony can you truly facilitate the active regeneration of both mind and body.

In *The Future of Growing Old* (published by Elsevier) Professor Polak describes his vision of aging a few decades from now, when:

> Elderly people will be young and stay so, till their breath of life snaps. One has to realise that a comparison between the elderly people of tomorrow and the old people of today will become impossible. Not only because one will live for 100 years, or even more, but because being old will be completely different from now.

It is that vision which the process of Facilitated Active Regeneration can help transform from a dream for the future into a reality for today.

Start working on your FAR programme right away. You will live never to regret it.

Appendix

Recommended Weights for Both Sexes by Age (in pounds)

Height	Years				
	20–29	30–39	40–49	50–59	60–69
4' 10"	84–111	92–119	99–127	107–135	115–142
4' 11"	87–115	95–123	103–131	111–139	119–147
5' 0"	90–119	98–127	106–127	114–143	123–152
5' 1"	93–123	101–131	110–140	118–148	127–157
5' 2"	96–127	105–136	113–144	122–153	131–163
5' 3"	99–131	108–140	117–149	126–158	135–168
5' 4"	102–135	112–145	121–154	130–163	140–173
5' 5"	106–140	115–149	125–159	134–168	144–179
5' 6"	109–144	119–154	129–164	138–174	148–184
5' 7"	112–148	122–159	133–169	143–179	153–190
5' 8"	116–153	126–163	137–174	147–184	158–196
5' 9"	119–157	130–168	141–179	151–190	162–201
5' 10"	122–162	134–173	145–184	156–195	167–207
5' 11"	126–167	137–178	149–190	160–201	172–213
6' 0"	129–171	141–171	153–195	165–207	177–219
6' 1"	133–176	145–188	157–200	169–213	182–225
6' 2"	137–181	149–194	162–206	174–219	187–232
6' 3"	141–186	153–199	166–212	179–225	192–238
6' 4"	144–191	157–205	171–218	184–231	197–244

Suggested further reading

Diet and vitamins
Benjamin, F. (1976) *No Aging Diet*; New York, Dial Press
Burkitt, D. (1979) *Don't Forget Fibre in Your Diet*; London, Martin Dunitz
Hanssen, M. (1984) *E For Additives*; Wellingborough, Thorsons
Holford, P. (1981) *The Whole Health Manual*; Bucks, Whole Health Programmes
Morgan, R. and Morgan R. (1986) *Brain Food*; London, Michael Joseph
Pauling, L. (1976) *Vitamin C, the Common Cold and the Flu*; San Francisco, W. H. Freeman and Company
Pauling, L. (1986) *How to Live Longer and Feel Better*; New York, W. H. Freeman and Company
Prevention Magazine Editors (1984) *The Complete Book of Vitamins*; Emmaus, Pa, Rodale Press
Stuart, R. B. and Davis, B. (1972) *Slim Chance in a Fat World*; Illinois, Research Press
Walker, C. and Cannon, G. (1984) *The Food Scandal*; London, Century Publishing
Wright, C. (1986) *The Wright Diet*; London, Piatkus

Longevity and health
Ardell, D. B. (1986) *High Level Wellness*; Berkeley, Ten Speed Press
Coleman, V. (1984) *Bodysense*; London, Thames and Hudson
Fogarty, M. (1975) *Forty to Sixty*; London, Centre for Studies in Social Policy

Kenton, L. (1985) *Ageless Ageing*; London, Century Publishers

Melville, A. and Johnson, C. (1985) *The Long-Life Heart*; London, Century Publishing

Myers, A. and Andersen, C. P. (1984) *Success Over Sixty*; New York, Summit Books

Pearson, D. and Shaw, S. (1982) *Life Extension*; New York, Warner Books

Puner, M. (1974) *To The Good Long Life*; New York, Universe Books

Popov, I. (1975) *Stay Young*; New York, Grosset and Dunlap

Rosenfeld, A. (1985) *Prolongevity II*; New York, Alfred Knopf

Stress and Anxiety

Berne, E. (1981) *What do You Say After You Say Hello?*; London, Corgi Books

Cox, T. (1986) *Stress*; London, Macmillan

Fensterheim, H. and Baker, J. (1976) *Don't Say Yes when you want to say No*; London, Futura

Harris, T. (1969) *I'm OK – You're OK: A Practical Guide to Transactional Analysis*; New York, Harper and Row

Jacobson, E. (1976) *You Must Relax*; London, Souvenir Press

Lewis, D. (1985) *Fight Your Phobia and Win*; London, Sheldon Press

Poteliakhoff, A. and Carruthers, M. (1981) *Real Health – the Ill Effects of Stress and their Prevention*; London, Davis-Poynter

Selye, H. (1976) *The Stress of Life*; New York, McGraw Hill

Sheehy, G. (1974) *Passages – Predictable Crises of Adult Life*; New York, E. P. Dutton

Exercise

Brannin, M. (1982) *Your Body in Mind*; London, Souvenir Press

Solomon, H. (1984) *The Exercise Myth*; London, Angus and Robertson

Mind developmennt

Lewis, D. and Greene, J. (1982) *Thinking Better*; New York, Holt, Reinhart and Winston

Lewis, D. and Greene, J. (1982) *Know Your Own Mind*; Harmondsworth, Penguin Books

Ostrander, S. and Schroeder, L. (1979) *Superlearning*; London, Souvenir Press

Wonder, J. and Donovan, P. (1984) *Whole-Brain Thinking*; New York, William Morrow

A cassette-tape training programme teaching the skills of relaxation has been recorded by Dr Lewis and can be obtained from Stresswatch, 8, The Avenue, Eastbourne, at a cost of £6.95 inclusive of VAT and postage.

Index

The Alpha Plan
Making the most of your mind

DAVID LEWIS

Do you ever have trouble recalling
information? Have you ever found
yourself flustered in a social situation?
Do you find it difficult to make decisions
when faced with a deadline? Have you
ever wanted to improve your sports
playing from mediocre to excellent?

The Alpha Plan can transform your
lifestyle. Psychologist David Lewis has
devised a set of specific yet straightforward
procedures which can be mastered in just
a few weeks. These techniques include
understanding the art of relaxation and
learning to recognise when your brain is
producing alpha waves and at its most
receptive.

With the Alpha Plan you will find it easier
to confront life's challenges and to
transform your setbacks into successes.

Also available in Methuen
Paperbacks

In and Out of Love
The mystery of personal attraction

DAVID LEWIS

Why do we like – even fall in love with –
or simply loathe some people, often
within moments of first meeting?

Is attraction based on looks, shared
opinions and temperament, an idealistic
imposition on the other person of all those
qualities one lacks but would like to have
– or even on smell?

In this imaginative and stimulating book,
psychologist David Lewis tells us not only
how this mystery affects love and
friendship, but how it is relevant in all
areas of life from the relationship between
parent and child, teacher and pupil,
interviewer and job-hunter, jury and
defendant, to, for example, the whole
question of racial intolerance.

How to Survive the 9 to 5

MARTIN LUCAS, KIM WILSON AND EMMA HART

Are you a sensation-seeking trapeze artist or a solitary novelist; extrovert or introvert; stable or unstable? Do you see changes at work in terms of a threat or a challenge? Do you think that a racing driver has a different stress level from a bored factory worker who feels that even 'a maggot could do this job'?

Whatever job you do, you are likely to go through periods of stress which could have lasting effects on your health, your career and your self-confidence. This fascinating and lively book looks at the latest ideas in dealing with stress at work, its causes and its effects, and investigates the interaction between personal responsibility and overload, the effect of social relationships and the impact of new attitudes and patterns of employment for men and women.

Based on the television series presented by Professor Cary Cooper, a leading expert on industrial stress, this book will help you, and the firm for which you work, to reduce job stress and increase job satisfaction.